Maths Game

Lynne Burgess

Bright Ideas
FOR Early Years

Published by Scholastic Publications Ltd,
Villiers House, Clarendon Avenue,
Leamington Spa, Warwickshire
CV32 5PR

© 1992 Scholastic Publications Ltd
Reprinted 1993

Written by Lynne Burgess
Edited by Janet Fisher
Sub-edited by Jane Wright
Illustrations by Emma Brown
Cover design by Anna Oliwa
Cover photograph by Martyn Chillmaid
Photographs by Garry Clarke

Artwork by Liz Preece,
Castle Graphics, Kenilworth
Printed in Great Britain by
The Alden Press Ltd, Oxford

British Library Cataloguing in Publication Data
A catalogue record for this book is available from the British Library.

ISBN 0-590-53042-9

Contents

Introduction

Mathematics is an intrinsic part of everyday life for early years pupils. At home, many quite ordinary activities help to develop a child's mathematical understanding — building with bricks can increase an awareness of space and solid shapes, helping with cooking offers opportunities to explore weight, time and numbers, while tidying toys away can involve a variety of sorting activities. In school, early years teachers are experienced at identifying the mathematical potential in many diverse areas of the curriculum.

One of the most popular vehicles for reinforcing mathematical skills is through the use of 'games'. This book aims to outline a wide variety of games covering many areas of the mathematics curriculum. I have chosen to interpret the word 'games' in its broadest sense so that floor games, and musical and PE activities are included as well as the more traditional table-top board games.

The purpose of mathematical games

Playing mathematical games can fulfil several objectives:
• They can be used to practise recently acquired skills. Placing a skill, such as the recognition of plane shapes, within a games situation provides pupils with a chance to name and recognise shapes in a more interesting context.
• Skills which have already been learned can be consolidated through games, while speed and accuracy can be increased. Counting is one such skill. Counting practical apparatus, cards,

pictures of objects, squares on a route, spots on a die and so on, places the skill in a whole host of different settings and helps pupils move from the 'touching each object' stage to the immediate recognition of a group of objects.
• Games can encourage an enthusiasm for mathematics. Early years teachers have become increasingly aware of the need to promote actively a positive attitude towards mathematics. Even some children as young as three or four acquire a negative attitude towards mathematics from adults or peers. Games can help make mathematics more appealing and help to rectify any negative preconceptions which a child may have already developed.
• Similarly, some children may acquire a stereotyped view that mathematical games are more appropriate for boys than for girls. Ensuring that all children can successfully take part in mathematical games may help redress any such attitudes.
• Often games can act as a bridge between practical activities and more abstract ideas or methods of recording. As many games can be adapted for play at different levels, the amount of concrete apparatus included can be geared to suit the ability of the pupils. For example, a game relating to length can be designed to give the pupils important firsthand experience of comparing the length of different materials.
• It is rare for any game to be played in silence, and so the relaxed atmosphere necessary for many games provides opportunities for pupils to use and extend their mathematical language.
• A games situation often promotes co-operation and encourages shy, reticent pupils to work with others in a group. Some pupils learn more quickly by working together than on their own as they articulate and discuss each other's ideas.

Advantages of classroom-made games

Although there are tremendous demands made upon teachers' non-contact time, it is worth seriously considering making your own games. Enlisting the help of ancillary helpers and parents can reduce your input. Here are some of the advantages:
- They generally cost less than commercial ones. Home-made games can help to make limited finances stretch just that little bit further.
- They can be made more relevant to particular pupils and their own environment. If you are finding it difficult to find games which relate to pupils in an inner city (or rural) environment, why not try making your own?
- Similarly, home-made games can be deliberately designed to reflect multicultural and non-sexist attitudes.
- It is possible to design mathematical games so that they can be adapted or extended to cover several stages within one small mathematical area. For example, number games can be designed for initial use with concrete apparatus, then changed to pictures and eventually to numerals and even number words. Thus, the same game can be replayed several times but with increasing mathematical demands.
- You can involve children in designing their own games. After some experience of commercial or teacher-made games, children will begin to develop a greater understanding of games and will be more able to contribute.
- The subject matter of classroom-made games can be specifically linked to current topic work. Many areas of the curriculum can be easily incorporated into a game. Try inventing one based on

a nursery rhyme, a song, a favourite story, an aspect of science (such as magnets, push and pull toys) or a map.

Points to remember when designing games

Before devoting a lot of time and materials to making a game, it is worth considering the following points:
- How many players? Obviously, very young children find it more difficult to cope with a large group and easily become bored and distracted if they have to wait a long time for their turn. The younger the children, the fewer players should be involved. However, it is very good experience to learn how to co-operate in a larger group (say four players).
- Size and scale. Make sure that all components are matched in size and scale to the pupils' needs. Once again, the younger the child, the larger the track, counters, cards, dice and so on.
- 'Real materials'. Bear in mind that with very young pupils, it is always best to include 'real materials' in a game and avoid too many abstract signs and

symbols. For example, practical apparatus and toys (farm animals, vehicles, Duplo) will be far more meaningful to the pupils than obscure signs and symbols which are beyond their mathematical stage of development.

• Visual appeal. Games need to be attractive to look at and pleasant to hold. Bright colours and simple, bold illustrations will increase their appeal. Check regularly the condition of games and make any necessary repairs.

• Relevance. Games need to be attractive to *all* pupils so it is important to take care not to reinforce gender stereotypes unintentionally nor be oblivious of our multicultural society. Look out for games from other countries or those which parents or grandparents used to play.

• Ensure success. It is essential to match the mathematical demands of the game to the abilities and skills of the pupils. A game which is too complicated or too difficult will give the children a sense of failure and alienate them from mathematics.

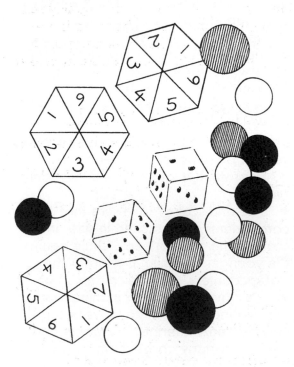

• Chance. Check the games to see whether a reasonable proportion of them include an element of chance. A balance needs to be achieved so that less able pupils have the opportunity to succeed.

• Attention span. Avoid creating a game which takes a long time to complete. The age and experience of the pupils will dictate the optimum length of a game.

• Competition versus co-operation. Once again, it is useful to assess regularly the games offered to pupils. Are the majority of them highly competitive with only one winner? Many games use a process of elimination to establish one winner and this can upset young children. Is it possible to include games which involve the children working in pairs or as part of a team?

• Quality materials. Good quality card, paper, felt-tipped pens and so on will result in improved visual appeal and extend the life of the game. Protect games with plastic film (or laminate them) to improve their durability and prevent them becoming tatty.

• Self-correcting. At the initial stage of design, always consider whether it is possible to make the game self-correcting. See examples in Greedy monsters on page 17 and Stack the shop shelves on page 18.

• Photocopying. If some components of the game need to be duplicated, access to a photocopier can save time. Several photocopiable sheets are available at the end of this book relating to the games outlined.

• Useful items of equipment. While it is sometimes valuable for the children to make their own die, playing cards or spinners, many educational suppliers now offer a wide range of these items, including blank ones which can easily be adapted. If you feel dissatisfied with your drawing skills, buy gummed pictures or rubber stamps from suppliers.

Alternatively, good pictures can sometimes be found in magazines, catalogues, wrapping paper, Christmas/birthday cards and so on.

Points to remember when using mathematical games

Consider the following points when organising and using games within the classroom:
- Space. Ensure that all players can see easily all the component parts of a game. If there is inadequate space on a table top, use the carpet area as an alternative. Floor games often need a large space which will not be in the way of other activities.
- Accessibility. Mathematical games should be easily accessible to the children so that they can fetch and return them with as little adult help as possible.
- Storage. Look out for suitable containers in which to store games. Ice cream tubs, large yoghurt pots with lids, biscuit tins, small plastic spice jars and small strong cardboard boxes are all very handy. Large cereal or washing powder boxes can be cut in half and covered in wallpaper. Plastic wallets with zips can be bought from educational

suppliers while small plastic baskets can be found in most DIY stores. Strong brown envelopes and even home-made card wallets are less durable but can make useful temporary storage.

Whatever the container, use clear, visible labels, preferably with picture clues for the youngest children. Colour coding with small sticky labels ensures that the various parts of a game are tidied away in the correct container. It is also useful to include a brief set of instructions inside the games box so that you can avoid too many interruptions from adult helpers.
- Adult supervision. There are several advantages to having an adult present throughout the game: firstly, when introducing a new game to explain the instructions and support those children lacking confidence; secondly, to promote the use of the correct mathematical vocabulary; thirdly, to encourage children to discuss what they are doing in a constructive way.
- Estimation. Try to create opportunities for the children to estimate. This is an important mathematical skill highlighted by the National Curriculum and is one which not only relates to number but to size, length, weight, time, capacity and so on.

Additional points

Pupils also need to be encouraged, and sometimes actively taught, to:
- Care for the equipment. Remember to praise children who handle games carefully and tidy them away in an orderly manner. If the children have contributed to the design and making of the game, they are likely to show more consideration.
- Develop social skills. Games are an ideal way of encouraging social skills and a respect for others. Remember to

congratulate pupils for taking turns politely, being patient with someone experiencing difficulties, helping each other, being a good loser and allowing someone else to start first. Furthermore, games can offer an ideal opportunity for children to give instructions and to teach each other.

• Agree on rules. Keep the number of rules to a minimum, but remember that all games rely on specific agreed rules. Sometimes very young children do not understand the need for consistent rules and they need to be encouraged to play 'fairly'. A class or group discussion about the need for 'rules' can help overcome this problem. Older pupils can change the rules of a well-known game or devise a totally new game with their own list of rules.

• Decide who will start the game. Some pupils will not worry about who starts a game while others will have a strong sense of fair play and feel the need to have an agreed way of deciding who has the first turn. If squabbles over this occur regularly, encourage the pupils to devise their own method for deciding.

• Moving along a track. This is more difficult than you may initially realise and not a skill which you can assume children have already acquired. A large floor track (made with pieces of paper or hoops) is often a good introduction. Ask the children to work in pairs, with one child as the counter and the other using a dice to determine how far the 'counter' child should move.

Conclusion

The games outlined in this book are merely a starting point and not meant to be purely prescriptive. Many will need to be adapted to suit your pupils while others may inspire you to design your own game. I have included some very well-known games to show newly-qualified teachers how simple ideas such as dominoes, snap and lotto can be adapted. I have also outlined some more unusual ideas which I hope will inspire more experienced teachers. It is inevitable that other teachers working on the same mathematical concepts may well have devised similar games and any resemblance is not intentional.

Organisation of the book

The games suggested in this book are grouped under mathematical areas such as sets, numbers and so on for ease of use. Each game follows a similar format, set out under the following headings:

Objective: A brief summary of the main mathematical area covered, although other areas could also be included incidentally.
Group size: To indicate whether the game is best restricted to two players or suitable for the whole class.
What you need: The equipment and materials necessary to play the game.
Preparation: Instructions on making components for the game.
What to do: Brief step-by-step instructions, together with any alternative ideas.
Discussion: Points to discuss before, during or after the game.

Colours

Chapter one

Colour recognition is an important skill which young children need to learn as soon as possible. As well as being the basis for much classroom organisation, it is an integral part of many mathematical activities such as sorting, matching and sequencing. Do not assume that children will have learned to recognise colours at home. Talking with children about the colours they choose when painting or encouraging them to match cups and saucers by colour are both examples of typical incidental activities which arise naturally as they play.

   Colours can also be reinforced in a games situation. Many boxed games and classroom equipment tend to use the primary colours; remember to include activities which discuss less obvious colours such as grey, brown, purple and pink. Similarly, include activities which ask the children to look at shades of one colour, so that they begin to recognise light and dark.

Flower circle

Objective
To reinforce colour recognition.

Group size
Whole class.

What you need
For the preparation: white card, scissors, a ruler, felt-tipped pens, plastic film, a hole punch, string.
For the game: a colour label for each child, a hall or large space.

Preparation
Cut white card into pieces about 20cm × 15cm. Draw a large simple flower on each card and colour it with one felt-tipped pen. Try to make each flower a different colour. Protect the cards with plastic film. Make two holes on the top edge of the label and tie on enough string so that the label can be hung around the child's neck.

What to do
● Show the children the flower cards and discuss the different colours. If you have made more than one card in any one colour, make sure the children know how many of each there are.

● Hold the cards with the flower face downwards and let each child choose a card. Ask each child to wear their flower label back to front so that they cannot see each other's flower. Initially, the children may have to practise putting their labels over their heads.
● Ask the children to hold hands and form a circle. Choose one child to stand in the middle.
● Ask the children to walk round, singing the following song to the tune of 'The Farmer's in his Den'.

(Name of child) wants a flower.
(Name of child) wants a flower.
Ee-i, Ee-i,
(Name of child) wants a flower.

● Invite the child in the circle to name a particular colour she would like and encourage the rest to continue singing:

(Name of child) wants a red one.
(Name of child) wants a red one.
Ee-i, Ee-i,
(Name of child) wants a red one.

● When the children have finished singing, ask them to stand still. Invite the child in the middle to ask another child, 'Have you got a red flower?' If the second child cannot remember the colour of her flower, let her look at it, without showing it to any of the other children. If the child replies, 'Yes, I have a red flower', ask her to turn over her label to reveal her flower but remain part of the circle. If, however, the child replies, 'No, I haven't got a red flower', let the child in the middle ask another child. If this reply is also negative, ask the two children to change places so that a new child is in the middle.
● Continue the game until all the children have revealed their flowers.

Discussion
Encourage the children to consider probability when naming a colour. If

there is one flower of each colour and the red flower has already been revealed, is there any point in asking for a red one again? Help them to realise that they need to choose a different colour each time. As the game nears the end, the range of colours to choose from will be reduced. Encourage the children to predict the likely colours of those left.

Dressing-up race

Objective
To reinforce colour recognition and to introduce pupils to shades of one colour.

Group size
Ideally eight but more if there is adequate space.

What you need
A hall, four plastic crates, one set of clothes per pair of children (the items of clothing should form sets of colours, such as one red hat, one red shirt, one red belt and one red bag), coloured paper squares and small paper hats to match the colours of the clothes.

What to do
• Put one item from each set of clothes into each crate.
• Place the four crates of mixed clothing in the four corners of the hall, allowing enough space for children to move all around them.
• Place the coloured squares of paper on the floor at one end of the hall, not too close together.
• Ask eight children to form pairs, and ask each pair to stand beside a crate. Invite one of each pair to close their eyes and choose a paper hat to determine what colour clothing they must collect. Also ask them to agree who is going to dress up.
• When you say, 'Go', let each pair of children search in the crate for an item of clothing in their chosen colour. When they have found one, let one child put it on, with assistance from the other if necessary. Once on, they must move round the room in sequence to the other crates.
• When the child is wearing all four items of clothing, tell both partners to stand beside their coloured square.
• Choose one of the following ways to finish the game: (a) when one pair is standing beside their square; (b) when all the pairs are standing beside their squares; (c) when a set period of time has elapsed. The children can then discuss the order in which they finished.

Discussion
What colours are being collected? Which items of clothing are easy or difficult to put on? Did the pupils manage to work together? Look at the range of shades of one colour. How many light colours? How many dark colours?

Clown colours

Objective
To reinforce colour recognition.

Group size
Two to four.

What you need
For the preparation: photocopiable page 89, felt-tipped pens, card, glue, plastic film, scissors, white card.
For the game: base boards, ten coloured card circles for each board.

Preparation
Make a photocopy of page 89 for each child and use different coloured felt-tipped pens to colour the clowns, ensuring that no two circles on one board are the same colour. Stick them on card and cover with plastic film.

Cut out circles from white card, the same size as the circles on the base boards. Colour one side with felt-tipped pens (to match the circles on the base board) and cover with plastic film.

What to do
• Ask each child to choose a clown board. Place the coloured circles face down in the middle of the table.
• Let each child take a turn to choose a circle, turn it over to reveal the colour and match it to his card, if possible. If the coloured circle does not match a circle on his board, he must return it.
• Continue the game until one child has completed her clown board. Encourage the other children to find the remaining coloured circles to complete their card.

Discussion
Where are the circles on the clown board? How many are there on the face, the hat, the tie? How many circles are there altogether? Can the pupils point to a specific coloured circle? Have all the clowns got a brown circle? Is the brown circle always in the same place on the clown?

Handling data

Chapter two

Mathematical games can offer children many opportunities to handle data in a practical context. Collecting, recording and processing information using real objects within an informal game situation can help to make data handling meaningful. The games in this chapter have been divided into two sections, Sorting and Tallying. Sorting involves classifying objects or pictures according to agreed criteria, while tallying usually involves collecting data and recording either with real objects or symbols. In both cases, it is important to encourage children to talk about the games so that they can interpret the information they have processed.

Sorting

Sorting into sets occurs naturally in many everyday situations, at home and at school. It is important to offer pupils a wide variety of sorting activities with commercially-available materials and objects collected by the pupils such as clothing, leaves and toys.

While many children find it fairly easy to sort objects according to colour, shape or size, some find it more difficult with other more unusual attributes. Games can provide an interesting way of extending the range of sorting criteria. The following games are intended to prompt pupils to think of less obvious ways of sorting and can easily be adapted.

Big bad troll

Objective
To explore different ways of sorting themselves into sets.

Group size
Whole class.

What you need
For the preparation: a paper plate, card, scissors, a ruler, a stapler, collage materials.

For the game: several long skipping ropes, four bean bags, one Big Bad Troll mask, a large space such as a hall, 'The Three Billy Goats Gruff' story.

Preparation
Add collage features to the paper plate to make a Big Bad Troll face. Staple the face onto a headband made from card. Make sure the headband will rest on the pupils' foreheads and will not obscure their vision.

What to do
• Prepare the children by getting them to sort themselves into sets in other situations. For example, when dismissing them from the room or asking them to line up, ask for 'the set of children with blue eyes/white socks/brown hair'. Once they can achieve this easily, choose a child to suggest the attributes.
• Read 'The Three Billy Goats Gruff' story to introduce the Big Bad Troll who is the main character in this game.
• Choose one child to be the Big Bad Troll and ask her to wear the mask.
• Ask the remainder of the class to stand at one end of the hall; the Troll should stand beside a pretend bridge, indicated by bean bags on the floor. Ensure the 'bridge' area is large enough for the number of pupils playing. Put the skipping ropes on the floor to form a large circle (a safe field) behind the bridge (see below).

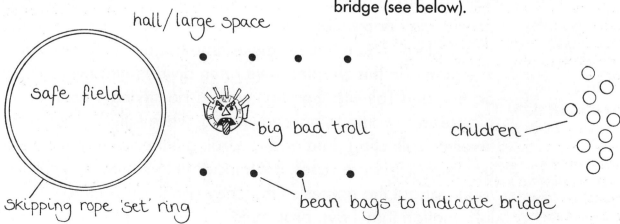

hall/large space

safe field

big bad troll

children

skipping rope 'set' ring

bean bags to indicate bridge

• Encourage the children to chant, 'Big Bad Troll, Big Bad Troll, may we cross your rickety bridge?' The Troll must reply, 'Only the set of children with : . .' and choose an attribute – blue eyes, long hair, white socks, jumpers, birthdays in September and so on. Those children who are members of the set should try to run across the bridge to the safety of the field on the other side without being caught by the Troll. If the Troll catches another child they must swop roles. After each attempt to cross the bridge, tell all the children to return to the starting positions.

Discussion
How many different ways of sorting themselves can the children devise? Suggest an impossible attribute – 'only the set of children with six heads' – to demonstrate the idea of an empty set with zero members.

Greedy monsters

Objective
To practise sorting pictures of objects using unusual attributes.

Group size
Two to four.

What you need
For the preparation: card, felt-tipped pens, plastic film, a pencil, scissors, Blu-tack, a cardboard box.
For the game: self-correcting cards, three monster heads.

Preparation
To make the self-correcting cards, divide a piece of card into six rectangles. In the rectangles draw simple pictures of objects with a common property, such as fruit or items of clothing. Before cutting into individual cards, draw one large picture of a similar item on the back. Colour and cover with film.

To make a monster head, turn a cardboard box upside down. Cut a mouth-shaped hole in one side and paint the box to look like a face. Use card or paper to add 3D features such as hair, ears and nose. For each head, cut a large pink tongue from strong card and write a different attribute on each, for example, 'I only eat fruit'. Fix the tongue with Blu-tack to the lower lip of the open mouth.

What to do
• Show the children the monster heads and explain that the 'tongue' label indicates what each monster likes to eat.
• Shuffle the small cards and place them face down in a pile. Let each child take turns to choose a card and post it through the mouth of the appropriate monster head.

● Once all the cards have been posted, lift up each monster head, remove the cards and ask the children to piece together the picture on the reverse side to form one large picture. In this way, the children can see if they have made any mistakes.

Discussion

Show the children the pictures on the small cards before playing to ensure that they can recognise each one. Encourage them to help each other if someone is unsure where to post a particular card. If there are any incorrect pieces in the puzzles at the end of the game, discuss where they belong.

Stack the shop shelves

Objective

To sort pictures of objects into sets.

Group size

Two to four.

What you need

For the preparation: a large, strong envelope, white card, felt-tipped pens, split pins, scissors, plastic film.

Figure 1

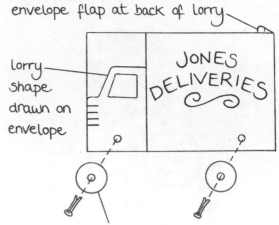

envelope flap at back of lorry

lorry shape drawn on envelope

JONES DELIVERIES

card wheels attached by split pins

For the game: a lorry envelope, four shop base boards, four sets of small 'goods' cards.

Preparation

Draw a large lorry shape on each side of the envelope. Cut two wheel shapes from the card and attach to the envelope with split pins (see Figure 1).

Using card and felt-tipped pens, make four baseboards, each representing a different type of shop. Each board should have six spaces onto which small 'goods' cards will fit (see below, left). Cover the baseboards with plastic film.

Use the card to make four sets of small cards depicting goods belonging to each shop. You will need to make six cards for each set. These sets of cards can be made self-checking by drawing one large picture of a similar item on the back before cutting out the individual cards. Cover the cards with plastic film.

What to do

● Before playing the game, explain to the children that the shops have sold all their goods and the shelves need to be refilled. Show several examples of the small cards to establish the fact that each belongs to a specific shop.

● Place all the small cards inside the

envelope 'delivery lorry' and the four base boards in the centre of the table. Decide whether to make the game co-operative with all the players helping each other to place the cards correctly, or competitive by allocating each child a specific shop, in which case each child must collect only those goods belonging to his shop and return unwanted cards to the 'delivery lorry'.

● Ask the players to take turns to take a small card from the envelope without looking. Once they have chosen a card, they should place it onto the correct base board 'shop'.

● Let the children check whether the cards have been correctly positioned by using the reverse of the allocated cards to make one large picture.

● Continue the game until one child has a full shop.

Discussion

Ask the children to suggest other items for each of the shops shown on the base boards. What other types of shops are the children familiar with? Can they name specific items which are sold in each one? Let the children look at all of the small cards and discuss whether there are other ways of sorting them by colour, shape, material, things we eat or wear.

Tallying

Tallying was a method of recording employed by early man and it is still a useful way of gathering and storing information. Tallying lends itself to making a count of objects which would prove difficult to physically group together. It is also a concept which can easily be reinforced through games.

Initially, it is important to use 'real' objects such as bricks, counters, beads, pegs, natural materials such as conkers, fir cones and pebbles to record the tally, before introducing them to the more abstract form using ЈΗΤ . Similarly, it is best to start with games where there are only two players so that children are only comparing two sets of information.

The following games will require a fairly large space such as a corridor, hall or playground.

Snowmen skittles

Objective

To reinforce the use of tallying and introduce it as a way of keeping a score in a game.

Group size

Pairs.

What you need

For the preparation: coloured sticky tape, card, felt-tipped pens, plastic or wooden skittles or plastic drink bottles, sand or water, scissors.

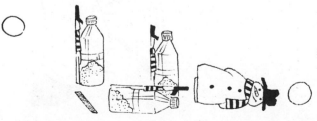

For the game: a ball, decorated skittles (these could be snowmen or other characters such as bears or clowns or if time is tight, use undecorated lightweight skittles), Unifix cubes.

Preparation

Draw six large snowmen on card. Colour them and cut them out. Stick them onto skittles or plastic bottles weighted down with sand or water.

What to do

• Use the coloured sticky tape to mark two lines on the floor, one to show where the children are to stand and one to indicate where to place the snowmen skittles. The distance between the two will obviously depend upon the age of the children; the younger the children, the shorter the distance. Explain the coloured lines to the pupils.

• Let each child take turns to throw the snowball (ball) at the snowmen skittles and try to knock down as many as possible.

• Encourage the children to place one Unifix cube beside each fallen skittle before replacing the skittles and joining the cubes together. Once the pupils are more familiar with the game, some may be able to count the fallen skittles and will not need to use the cubes.

• Finish the game in one of these ways. Decide on a number of throws for each child, matched to the age and experience of the pupils. After the agreed number of throws, ask the players to compare the length of the sticks of Unifix.

Alternatively, decide on a score to be reached, also depending on the age and experience of the pupils. Very young pupils could be asked to place their cubes onto a score-card and the game would end once a player had covered all the snowmen on the score-card.

Discussion

Why is tallying a good method for recording the score in this game? Can they suggest other pieces of equipment in the classroom which could be used instead of the Unifix? Compare their scores and incorporate vocabulary such as 'more', 'less', 'fewer' and 'same' into the discussion.

Feed the robot

Objective
To reinforce the use of ⲒⲎⲦ as a method of tallying for keeping a score.

Group size
Pairs.

What you need
For the preparation: a cardboard box, coloured sticky tape, paint, cardboard tubes, a stapler, card, scissors.
For the game: a cardboard box robot head (or use the Greedy Monster head with the top cut open — see page 17), five red bean bags, five blue bean bags, a chalkboard, blue and red chalk.

Preparation
Cut the top off a medium-sized cardboard box. Paint a simple robot face on the front. Paint two cardboard tubes and stick them onto the inside of the box to look like aerials. Staple a cardboard dial to one side of the box with an arrow to indicate when the robot is hungry.

What to do
• Use the coloured sticky tape to mark two lines on the floor, one to show where the children should stand and one to indicate where to place the robot head. The distance between the two lines will depend upon the age and ability of the pupils. Explain the lines to the pupils.
• Give one player five red bean bags and red chalk, and the other five blue bean bags and blue chalk.
• Ask one child to turn the arrow on the robot head dial to indicate that the robot is hungry.
• Encourage each child to write her name on the chalkboard.
• Let each child take turns to feed the robot with microchips (bean bags) by trying to throw them into the robot head

box. Show the children how to make a tally on the chalkboard for each bean bag which lands in the box.
• Finish the game in one of these ways:
(a) Decide on a number of throws for each child, matched to the age and experience of the pupils. After the agreed number of throws, let the two players compare the number of tally marks.
(b) Decide on a score to reach, again depending on the age and experience of the pupils.
(c) At the end of the game, ask a child to turn the dial on the robot box head to 'not hungry'.

Discussion
When counting their scores, encourage the children to count in fives. Is it easier to count tallies which have been organised into groups of five by 'crossing the gate', for example, ⲒⲎⲦ rather than one long line of tally marks, for example, ||||| ? Can the children estimate what score they think they will achieve in each turn? Let the children experiment with the distance between them and the robot head. If the distance is greatly increased, what happens to their score, and vice versa?

Traffic lights

Objectives
To use $\cancel{||||}$ as a method of tallying and to extend the amount of information compared to three sets.

Group size
Three.

What you need
For the preparation: red, orange, green and black sugar paper, coloured sticky tape, scissors, a black felt-tipped pen, glue, paper, paper-clips.
For the game: a traffic lights poster, a large sponge ball, a score-card.

Preparation
Stick three large coloured circles (red, orange and green) onto a large piece of black sugar paper, as in traffic lights. Number each circle: 3 on red, 2 on amber and 1 on green. The circles need to be large enough for the children to hit relatively easily and not too closely spaced together.

The score-card can be made quite simply using paper and pen, or you may try to elaborate as shown in Figure 1.

What to do
- Pin the traffic lights poster to a wall where there is easy access and adequate space to play.
- Line the sticky tape on the floor a short distance from the poster to indicate where the players should stand. The younger the child, the shorter the distance should be.
- Let each player take turns to throw the ball at the poster, aiming at the coloured circles. If a child hits a circle, she must record a score (1, 2 or 3) on the score-card using tally marks. If the ball misses, no tallies should be scored.
- Let the game continue until one player gains an agreed number of tallies. Comparing scores is easier if each pupil records one set of five tallies in each box on the score-card.

Discussion
Make sure the children interpret the information on their score-card correctly. Discuss the reason for recording only five tallies in each box. How does this make comparing the information easier?

Figure 1

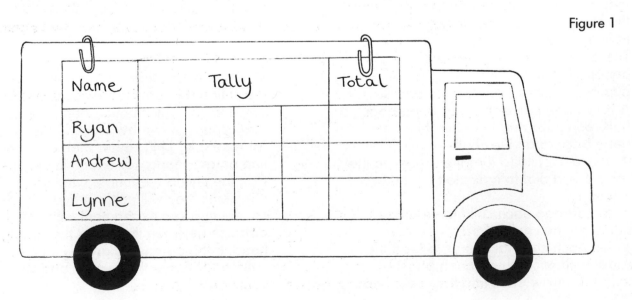

Name	Tally			Total
Ryan				
Andrew				
Lynne				

Shapes

Chapter three

It is important to foster children's awareness of shape, both two and three dimensional, and help them develop precise vocabulary so they can express their knowledge and understanding about shape. However, it is equally as important not to confuse plane and solid shapes. While you can discuss plane shapes in relation to the faces of solid shapes, do not, for example, call a cube-shaped brick a square. Any object which can be picked up is a solid shape while a plane shape is an abstract idea or the name of a face of a solid.

Games can provide another vehicle for exploring shapes and the following suggestions have been categorised into two groups — those associated with two-dimensional shapes (plane) and those dealing with three-dimensional shapes (solid).

Plane shapes

Young children are surrounded by shapes in their everyday lives and many will have explored them at home through toys such as puzzles, bricks and mosaics. These experiences can be continued and extended at school through art activities such as printing, painting, taking rubbings and via more direct shape-matching activities such as sorting, partitioning and ordering. Provide young children with a variety of concrete apparatus to explore the tactile as well as the visual aspects of shapes.

The games will build upon the children's existing knowledge and help introduce accurate mathematical language such as the names of common shapes together with the vocabulary used to describe them such as edge, curved, straight and corners.

The shape house

Objectives
To introduce the names of the common plane shapes and relate these to pictures of familiar objects.

Group size
Small group or whole class.

What you need
For the preparation: a small wooden brick, sticky labels, card, a pencil, felt-tipped pens, plastic film, a Stanley knife, masking tape.
For the game: a shape house, a shape die.

Preparation
Draw a large outline of a house on card. Draw doors and windows from shapes which are to be introduced. Include large and small ones of each shape, if appropriate. Colour and cover in plastic film. Use a Stanley knife to cut round each shape, leaving one edge to act as a hinge. Cut a piece of card large enough to cover the back of each window and draw on a picture of something which corresponds to each shape. Cover with film and stick each picture behind the relevant door or window.

Using a wooden brick and sticky labels, make a die with a different plane shape (as on the house) on four faces and leave two faces blank.

What to do
Staple the shape house to a display board and group the children around it so that they can all see easily.
• Taking turns, invite each child to throw the die and name the shape which appears uppermost. Ask them to decide whether they want to choose the large or small version of that shape to open on the shape house. The child should then

indicate where that shape appears on the picture. If the child throws a blank face, the die passes to another player.
• Once the picture has been revealed, the child must close the door or window and pass the die to another player.
• Continue the game until, either all the windows and doors have been opened, or for as long as you think appropriate.

Discussion

As each shape window or door is opened, discuss the properties of each shape. Is it large or small? How many edges has it? Are they curved or straight? Can the children find something in the room which is the same shape? Look carefully at the picture behind the door or window. Can the children suggest an alternative picture which could have been used to illustrate that shape?

Shape fish

Objective
To reinforce matching shape to shape.

Group size
Two to four.

What you need
For the preparation: white card, felt-tipped pens, scissors, ruler, a used matchstick.
For the game: a spinner with a choice of plane shapes, photocopiable page 90, coloured pencils.

Preparation
To make the spinner, cut an hexagonal shape from the card. Divide it into six equal sections. Within each section draw a different plane shape in a different colour. These shapes should match those on photocopiable page 90 (or your worksheet if you are using your own). Push the matchstick through the centre of the hexagon to form the pivot point.

What to do
• Give each child a copy of photocopiable page 90 or your own worksheet and make sure they are familiar with each of the shapes shown.
• Taking turns, ask each child to spin the spinner.

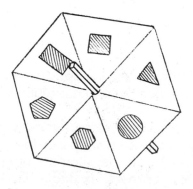

- He should then colour in on his fish a shape indicated by the spinner. If the spinner stops at a shape all of which have been coloured, the child must pass the spinner on to the next player without colouring in anything.
- Continue the game until a child has coloured all the shapes on the worksheet.

Discussion
Ask the children to point to a named shape on their worksheet. Can they name a shape which you indicate? How many of each shape can they count? Which shapes have curved or straight edges? How many shapes have four corners?

Biscuit fun

Objective
To reinforce understanding of the attributes of plane shapes.

Group size
Two to four.

What you need
For the preparation: card, felt-tipped pens, scissors, plastic film.
For the game: a large base board, small shape attribute cards, a plate, a die, plastic figures.

Preparation
On a piece of card, draw a simple track and draw 'smiley faces' in some of the squares. Cover with film.
   Cut different small shapes from card and make them look like biscuits. Cover with film.
   Cut a set of square cards and write on each the name of a shape or the attributes of a shape, such as curved edges, four corners, six edges. Cover the cards with plastic film.

What to do
- Place the base board and plate of card biscuits in the middle of the table. The cards containing the attributes should be placed in a pile, face down, at the side of the base board.
- Give each child a plastic figure for a counter and ask them to place it anywhere on the track at the start of the game.
- Invite the players to take turns throwing the die to indicate how many squares they can move their figure, in any direction.
- Each player must try to land on a square with a 'smiley face'. When a player succeeds, let her pick a small card from the top of the pile. This will either name a shape or give an attribute (such as 'six edges') which she must then find in the plate of biscuits. If she cannot find the correct biscuit, she must miss a go. Any incorrect biscuits must be returned to the plate. If she does find the correct biscuit, she can keep it.

- At the end of each turn, ask the children to return the small card to the bottom of the pile.
- Continue the game until one child has collected three biscuits which are the same shape. Modify the number of shapes and the variety of attributes to suit the experience and ability of the children. The number of biscuits to be collected will depend on the pupils' concentration span.

Discussion
Before starting the game, look closely with the children at the biscuit shapes to establish that they are familiar with the names and attributes of each shape. Also make sure they can read the attribute cards and sort out the range of biscuits to which each one applies. For example, four corners could apply to both oblongs and squares and it is important that the children realise this.

Solid shapes

Playing with bricks can increase a child's awareness about which solid shapes will build into a tower and which just fall off. A wide range of constructional activities using commercially-available kits, together with modelling junk materials, will help provide the essential first-hand experience of solid shapes. After considerable free play with solid shapes in a variety of materials, you could gradually introduce the correct names for each shape – cube, cuboid, cone, cylinder, pyramid, triangular prism, hexagonal prism, sphere. Make opportunities to discuss their particular properties and compare similarities and differences.

The following games can be used to reinforce and extend the children's ideas about solid shapes. It is essential for them to have practical experience as outlined above before playing these games.

Hiding bricks

Objective
To improve tactile recognition of solid shapes.

Group size
A small group or whole class.

What you need
A variety of bricks which reflect the solid shapes being taught, a small basket, a large space.

What to do
Ask the children to form a circle, standing with their hands behind their backs.
● Place at least six bricks in the basket, initially choosing only two different shapes. As the children become familiar with the game, include a wider range of solid shapes.
● Choose one child to hold the basket and ask him to walk round the outside of the circle placing a brick in each child's hand. Ask the rest of the class to chant (or sing):

> (Child's name, sung twice) where are the bricks?
> Why are you playing such a naughty trick?

until all the bricks have been placed in the children's hands. You should then chant (or sing), 'Who's got the cuboids?' (or any other solid shape).

The child (or children) holding the named solid shape must hold it up in the air and chant (or sing), 'I've got the cuboid'.
● At the end of the game, ask the children to return the bricks to the basket. Repeat the game with a different child giving out the bricks. Alternatively, you could change the bricks in the basket.

Discussion
Encourage the children to guess their shape by feeling and not looking. Are some shapes easier to identify than others? Can the children explain how they can identify their shape? Help them by including vocabulary such as curved, straight, faces and points in the discussions.

Solid shape tiddlywinks

Objective
To improve the ability to match a two-dimensional representation with a solid shape.

Group size
Two to four.

What you need
For the preparation: card, felt-tipped pens, plastic film.
For the game: large counters (a different colour for each player), a base board, a selection of solid shape bricks.

Preparation
Divide a large piece of card into equal-sized bands. Make sure the bands are large enough to flick counters on fairly easily. Colour the outside bands red and each of the other bands a different colour. Draw (or rubber stamp) a different solid shape in each of the coloured bands that are not red. Cover with plastic film.

What to do
● Ask the players to sit opposite each other with the base board in the middle and give each child a selection of the same coloured counters.
● Let the players take turns to use the counters like tiddlywinks, starting on the outside red band and flicking them onto the coloured bands. If a counter lands completely within a band, the player has to find a solid shape brick which matches the picture for that band. No brick is collected if the counter lands across two bands.
● Finish the game in a variety of ways:
(a) When one player has collected a specified number of solid shapes. Vary the number to suit the concentration span of the pupils.
(b) When one player has collected a specified number of different solid shapes. Again, take the children's ability into account.
(c) When one player has collected three shapes which are all the same.

Discussion
Is it easier to land a counter on some bands more than others? Does the children's skill improve with practice? Encourage the pupils to name and count the faces on their solid shapes. How many solid shapes have circles on their faces? Can the children find other examples of their solid shapes in the classroom?

30

Slippery slide

Objective
To explore solid shapes which will roll and/or slide.

Group size
Pairs.

What you need
For the preparation: card, felt-tipped pens, plastic film.
For the game: a smooth piece of wood, a cardboard box, a variety of different shaped bricks, a set of cards depicting those solid shapes, a large picture of Mr Roly Poly and one of Mr Slide.

Preparation
Use the card and felt-tipped pens to make a set of small cards depicting the solid shapes that will be encountered during the game. Make two large pictures, one of Mr Roly Poly and one of Mr Slide, as shown above. Each picture should be large enough to place on it five bricks. Cover the pictures with plastic film.

31

What to do

● Before the game starts, make sure the children understand the difference between sliding and rolling.

● Set up the slide on the carpet area by balancing the piece of wood against the cardboard box. Place the small cards face down next to the slide with the selection of bricks nearby. Turn the pictures of Mr Roly Poly and Mr Slide face down and let the players each choose one.

● Invite the players to take turns to choose a small card and find a solid shape which corresponds to the picture. Encourage them to predict whether the brick will roll or slide before trying it out. Once they have predicted, invite them to test the brick on the slide. The player can keep the brick if it belongs to his picture, for instance, if the player has the Mr Roly Poly picture, she can only keep the bricks which roll. All other bricks have to be returned to the original pile.

● Let the game continue until a player has found five bricks which belong to her picture.

Discussion

Encourage the players to think about which face of the solid shape they will place on the slide. For example, a cylinder will roll when placed in one position but slide if placed in another. Can the children recognise that some shapes can belong to both pictures? How many shapes can belong on both pictures? What are the similarities of shapes which will only slide?

Space: position vocabulary

Chapter four

It is very important for young children to extend and improve the accuracy of the positional language which they use. They may not normally use words such as in between, above, below, beside, next to, nearest and furthest. The ability to understand and use such terms appropriately is essential if they are to progress with mathematical areas such as shape and space. A wide range of positional vocabulary can be introduced through movement lessons or incidentally as children handle play equipment. Occasionally, it is useful to highlight particular vocabulary by playing games.

The games in this chapter offer an opportunity to reinforce and assess the children's ability to use positional vocabulary accurately.

Pinning the tail on the donkey

Objective
To reinforce positional vocabulary such as on, next to/beside, above, below/under, in between, nearest, furthest.

Group size
A small group or the whole class.

What you need
A large picture of a donkey (a simple outline on card covered with transparent plastic film), Blu-tack, five different coloured tails (cut from card and covered with plastic film), a blindfold.

What to do
• Display the picture of the donkey on an easily accessible wall at child height.

• Make sure the children realise where the donkey's tail ought to be. (A large red spot on the picture of the donkey usually helps avoid disagreement.)
• Blindfold a volunteer, spin him round and ask him to place a tail (using Blu-tack) onto the donkey.
• Repeat this with other volunteers and the remaining tails until all the tails have been attached.

Discussion
After each tail has been placed on the donkey, discuss its position. Where is it in relation to the various parts of the donkey? Also, discuss the position of each tail in relation to the other tails. For example, the yellow one is in between the red and blue one. Finally, discuss which tail is nearest/furthest from the red spot. With practice, the children will be able to describe the position of the tail without too much support.

Tickly spiders

Objective
To reinforce positional vocabulary (such as on, back, under and top) and directional vocabulary (such as up, down, along and round).

Group size
Whole class.

What you need
No specific requirements.

What to do
• Ask the children to find a partner and stand together. Choose a child as your partner.
• Explain that one child must stand still while the other acts out the movements to accompany a short story.
• Ask the second child to make her hand into the shape of a spider.
• Tell a brief story about the movements of the spider, for example:

'A spider scuttled along the ground, jumped on to a shoe and crawled slowly up the back of a leg. When he reached the waist, he tiptoed round to the tummy. Then he climbed up the chest and sat on the shoulder. He slid down the arm and landed with a bump on the hand. Quickly, he climbed back up to the shoulder and walked under the chin and round to the back of the neck. He crept up to the top of the head, jumped onto the nose and gave the child a tickle. The child shouted, 'Go away', and the spider fell down to the ground and scuttled quickly away.'

As you tell the story, demonstrate the movements on your partner and encourage the children to follow the movements.
• The children should then swap over and repeat the game.

Discussion
Discuss and name the various body parts before or after the story. As the children become more experienced, change the movements or ask the children to suggest ideas or even make up their own story.

Tell a journey

Objective
To develop the ability to give and receive complex positional and directional instructions.

Group size
A small group.

What you need
For the preparation: card, felt-tipped pens, plastic film.
For the game: small plastic figures to act as counters for each child, a base board, constructional toys, toy farm equipment and figures made from Plasticine to act as landmarks, small cards with pictures of landmarks.

Preparation
Draw a large simple route map on a piece of card. Cover it with film and place the small toys and Plasticine on it as landmarks. Make a set of small cards, each with a picture of one of the landmarks on it.

What to do
- Talk about the base board with the children to make sure they realise what each landmark is meant to be. Show them the small cards and ask individuals to match them to each landmark.
- Place the small cards face down in a pile beside the board. Ask the first player to take the first two cards from the top of the pile. These cards indicate the start and finish of the journey and may be used in any order.
- Let the first player put her plastic figure on the pathway next to the starting landmark and ask her to move it along any route to the finishing landmark. As she does so, she must tell the story of the journey. Which landmarks does she pass? What does she see? Does she stop to visit any of the landmarks on her journey and why? What is the purpose of her journey? What does she do at the finishing landmark?
- Let each player make a journey and tell the story to the group.

Discussion
Initially, children will need to be prompted by the teacher and encouraged to use positional and directional vocabulary. Ask them to think carefully about wording their instructions. Are these absolutely clear or could they be confusing? How could this be avoided? With more experience the children will be able to make their journeys more interesting and their stories more elaborate. If necessary, keep the base board very simple to start with and gradually add more landmarks. Invite the pupils to make their own landmarks out of LEGO, Duplo, bricks or Plasticine. The 'listening' players can be encouraged to make suggestions or ask questions while each child describes her journey.

Number

Chapter five

Early years pupils can be poles apart in understanding number. A three-year-old may be able to match one to one correctly with a small number of objects while many six-year-olds can add and subtract numbers to ten competently. The games suggested in this chapter have been grouped into sections covering some of the important stages in understanding number. Early number skills such as one-to-one correspondence and the concept of the terms 'more' and 'less' are covered in the first two sections. These are followed by games which reinforce counting and ordering numbers to ten. A section has also been devoted to the difficult concept of conservation for which games can provide a useful supporting activity. The final two sections include games which reinforce and extend simple addition and subtraction.

One-to-one correspondence

Matching one-to-one is an important skill which is essential for understanding number. Young children tend to be influenced by the way things look and it is a common error for young children to believe that there are more in one set of objects than another purely because the first set takes up more space than the second. Comparing two sets in one-to-one correspondence gives children a visual check to discover whether there are the same, more or fewer members.

Many practical activities arise naturally in everyday activities and an experienced adult will use these to improve the children's understanding. For example, asking questions about common play activities can lead the children to consider one-to-one correspondence — are there enough spades in the sand tray or painting aprons for a specific group of children?

Games such as the following offer the children the chance to practise matching one-to-one in a variety of contexts.

Flies in webs

Objective
To practise one-to-one correspondence, using themselves.

Group size
Whole class.

What you need
For the preparation: black sugar paper, a stapler, card.
For the game: five spider hats, large hoops, a tambourine, a large space.

Preparation
Cut a spider shape from the sugar paper and staple it onto a simple card headband.

What to do
• Choose five children to wear the spider hats. Place the hoops on the floor, well spaced out.
• Explain that the five spiders must try to capture the other children who must pretend to be flies and put one into each of their webs (the hoops). Once a fly has been placed in a web, ask him to stand with his legs apart. In this way, he can be rescued by another fly crawling through his legs. He can then rejoin the other flies flying around the hall.
• At regular intervals, shake the tambourine as a signal for everyone to stand still. Ask the children not in hoops to check which webs have been matched with a fly.
• Continue the game until all the webs are matched with a fly or as long as you want. Occasionally, stop the game and give other children a turn at being the spiders.

Discussion
Make sure the children understand the procedure for capture so as to avoid any rough behaviour. It is usually best to suggest the spiders only touch the flies lightly and lead them gently to a web while the flies, in turn, must go willingly once caught. Encourage the pupils to work co-operatively by trying to rescue as many captured flies as possible.

Toys' picnic

Objective
To practise one-to-one correspondence by matching real objects.

Group size
Four.

What you need
For the preparation: a strong cardboard box, scissors, rope, card, felt-tipped pens, plastic film.
For the game: four base boards, a picnic basket, four dolls or teddies, four different coloured sets of picnic equipment (knife, fork, spoon, plate, beaker), four sets of picnic food (such as crisps, apples, sandwiches).

Preparation
For the picnic basket, cut a flap in the top of the cardboard box, so that a child can get his hand in and out easily. Add rope handles and decorate to look like a basket.
   For the base boards, draw pieces of cutlery, crockery and items of food (the same number on each card) on pieces of card (about 30cm × 20cm). Colour in the items, using a different colour for each card. Cover with film.

What to do
• Ask each child to choose one teddy or doll. Colour code each one with a coloured ribbon or badge.
• Invite each child to find the base board which has the corresponding coloured equipment.
• Place the picnic basket in the middle of the table.
• Let the children take turns to put their hand into the picnic basket and, without looking, take out one object which they must place on their base board. If they pick an object which they already have or one which does not match the colour of their base board, they should return it to the basket.
• Let the game continue until one player has all the items for his picnic.

Discussion
Have all the teddies/dolls got a plate? Which teddies/dolls still need a cake? What is missing from your teddy's/doll's picnic? Can the children tell the colour of an object just by touch? Which other items can be added to the game?

Feeding time

Objective
To practise matching one-to-one and to compare sets.

Group size
Four.

What you need
For the preparation: card, felt-tipped pens, scissors.
For the game: sixty-four small picture cards, photocopiable page 91.

Preparation
Cut out sixty-four small cards, each to fit one of the squares on photocopiable page 91. On each card draw a picture of a worm, a cake, a carrot or a leaf. There should be sixteen of each.

What to do
• Give each child a photocopy of page 91 and five small picture cards. Place the remaining cards face down in a pile in the middle of the table.
• Ask the players to look at their cards and decide which set they have most of. Ask them to place these in the appropriate space on the base board. Explain that they must collect these cards. They should hold the remaining cards in a fan shape so that no one else can see.
• Invite the first player to ask another player for a card which he is collecting. If that player has a card, she must hand it over. Only one card is given at a time. If not, the first player must take a card from the top of the pile. If the player needs this card, he can place it on his base board. If not, he must keep it with the other cards in his hand.
• Continue the game until one player has four cards in a row horizontally, for example, he has a leaf for each caterpillar.

Discussion
Make sure each player understands which food is eaten by each animal on the base board. During and after the game, encourage the pupils to look at their base board and discuss the state of play. Have all the children got a cake? How many more worms are needed for each bird to have one? Do they have more leaves or more carrots on their board? Through discussion, help them to develop strategies for play. For example, if they already have three leaves on their base board, does it make sense to ask another player for a worm?

More and less

The terms 'more' and 'less' (some people prefer 'fewer') are used a great deal in mathematics and, for some children, these terms prove surprisingly difficult to assimilate. Whereas most children frequently use the word 'more' to describe situations comparing two sets, not many children understand or use the words 'less' or 'fewer'. Obviously, the games in the previous section can help develop an understanding of these words. Similarly, many opportunities exist in everyday activities which you can highlight to promote these words.

However, after a great deal of experience with concrete materials and matching one-to-one, it is sometimes useful to continue reinforcing these terms with games.

Sausage on a plate

Objective
To reinforce the terms 'more' (or 'less') using concrete apparatus.

Group size
Four.

What you need
Eight paper (or toy) plates, Plasticine, small cards (two for each player) of the following – 1 more, 2 more, 3 more.

What to do
• Give each child two paper plates and a ball of Plasticine. Spread the small cards face down in the middle of the table.
• Ask each child to make between one and five Plasticine sausages. Then invite them to choose one small card from the table. Make sure each child can read her card. Challenge them to make Plasticine

sausages for the second plate but following the instruction on their card. For example, if the card has '1 more' written on it, one plate must have one more sausage than the other.
• Encourage them to check each other's plates at the end.

Discussion
Can the children suggest a way of checking to see if they have followed the instructions on the card, that is, by moving the sausages off the plates and matching them one-to-one? Does anyone suggest checking by counting the number of sausages on each plate? Who has most or least sausages?

Spin the apples

Objective
To reinforce the terms 'more' and 'less' using pictures of objects.

Group size
Pairs.

What you need
For the preparation: photocopiable page 92, card, plastic film, glue, white card, scissors, felt-tipped pens.
For the game: two base boards, twenty 'apple' discs.

Preparation
Make two copies of photocopiable page 92 and mount each one on card. Cover with plastic film.

Cut twenty discs from the white card and draw pictures of apples on both sides of each disc (a different number on each side). Cover the discs with plastic film.

What to do
● Give each player a base board. Place the discs in a pile in between the two players.

● Explain the base board to the children. The picture of the happy face represents a child who always receives the most apples, while the sad face represents a child who always receives the least apples.
● Let the players take turns to take the top two discs from the pile. They must spin the discs and let them fall on the table. They should then look carefully at the apples on the discs to discover which disc has more. The disc with more apples should be placed under the happy face and the disc with less apples under the sad face. If both discs show the same number of apples, they must be returned to the bottom of the pile.
● Let the game continue until one player has filled her base board. Ask each player to count the total number of apples under the happy face to see who has more.

Discussion
During the game, encourage the children to talk about what is happening and help them use the terms 'more' and 'less' appropriately.

Buzzy bees

Objective
To reinforce the terms 'more' and 'less' using pictures.

Group size
Pairs.

What you need
For the preparation: white card, plastic film, felt-tipped pens, a large die, scissors. For the game: two base boards, eighteen card bees, a bee die.

Preparation
To make the base boards, draw a large simple picture of a flower with five petals onto each of two pieces of card. Make sure the petals are large enough for the card bees to be placed on them. Cover the cards with plastic film.

Using the white card, make eighteen card bees, three each with 0, 1, 2, 3, 4 and 5 stripes as illustrated. You will also need to cover each face of a die with a bee with a different number of stripes.

What to do
• Give each player a base board. Place the card bees face down in between the players.
• Let each child take turns to choose a bee and then throw the die. If the card bee has more stripes than the bee on the die, the player must place it on one of the petals of the flower. If the card bee has less stripes than the bee on the die, or if both bees have the same number of stripes, the card bee must be returned to the pile face down.
• Let play continue until one player has covered all of her petals with bees.

Discussion
Make sure the children understand that they are to look at the black stripes on the bees' bodies. Talk to them while they are playing and encourage them to use the appropriate vocabulary — more, less, the same as, etc. Younger players may use bees with stripes from 0 to 5 while more able children may be capable of using bees with stripes from 6 to 10.

Cardinal numbers

Number is an abstract idea and young children need to encounter a wide range of activities before they really understand numbers. Even though a child may be able to chant one, two, three, it is important to make sure that they have acquired a comprehensive understanding of numbers before moving on to harder concepts. For example, some children can chant the numbers as they move several objects at a time without making the necessary one-to-one correspondence of number name to object. Practical activities are essential. Touching each object as they say the number name will often require an adult's help. Similarly, it is important to teach young children how to organise their counting so that, for example, if they are counting a row of objects, they learn to start at one end of the row and finish at the other. When objects are arranged at random, children find it far more difficult to count them systematically. The ability to match the number symbol to the number name is another important step but it often takes some time before a child realises that the spoken numeral refers to the whole set of objects and not just the last one counted.

The following games offer opportunities for children to develop their understanding of number. Some teachers prefer to introduce and consolidate numbers to 5 before going on to numbers 6 to 10 so the sections are organised to correspond to this familiar teaching pattern. However, many of the games in the 0 to 5 section could equally be adapted for numbers 6 to 10.

Numbers 0 to 5

Eggs in a nest

Objective
To reinforce counting 0 and 2 using concrete apparatus.

Group size
Two or four.

What you need
For the preparation: paper plates, brown paper, glue.
For the game: nests, modelling dough or Plasticine, a die labelled with two spots on three faces (the rest blank).

Preparation
Cover the paper plates with brown paper and stick strips of paper around the edges to look like nests.

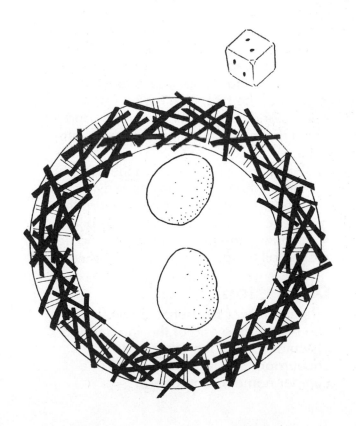

What to do
• Give each player three nests and a lump of dough or Plasticine.
• Let each player take turns to throw the die. If two spots appear on the uppermost face, ask the child to make two eggs with the dough and place them in one nest. If the die is blank, the child doesn't make any eggs and must pass the die to the next player.
• Continue the game until one player has filled each nest with two eggs.
• Adapt the game by changing the number of spots on the die.

Discussion
Make sure the players touch each egg (or spot on the die) as they count. Use the word zero to describe the blank faces on the die and hopefully, the children will copy. During the game, pause to count how many nests each player has filled and how many more are still empty.

Candles on the cake

Objectives
To practise counting numbers 0 to 5, matching concrete apparatus to number symbol. Also to organise the concrete apparatus in a line and to establish a start and finish point.

Group size
Two or four.

What you need
For the preparation: photocopiable page 93, card, felt-tipped pens, glue, scissors, plastic film, a chinagraph pen.

For the game: two to four base boards, fifty-four card candles, a set of small cards (two each numbered 0 to 5).

Preparation
Colour each cake on photocopiable page 93 a different colour. Mount on card and cover with plastic film. Using a chinagraph pen on the plastic film, write a number from 0 to 5 on each cake, but not in order.

Cut out a set of cards numbered 0 to 5 (two of each number). Cover with plastic film.

Cut out fifty-four candles from card. Colour them brightly and cover with plastic film.

What to do
● Give each child a base board. Encourage them to look at each cake on their board and name the number symbol.
● Place the number cards in a pile in the middle of the table and spread out the card candles.
● Let each player take turns to pick a number from the top of the pile. If that number appears on one of his cakes, he must return the number card to the bottom of the pile, take the corresponding number of candles and place them in a line on the appropriate cake.
● If a player does not have the number shown on the card or has already placed candles on that cake, he must return the number card to the bottom of the pile.
● Continue the game until one child has placed all the candles on all his cakes.

Discussion
Why is it easier to count the candles if you start at one end of the line and work systematically to the other end? Encourage the children to count one number name to one object.

Numbers 6 to 10

Musical bean bags

Objective
To reinforce counting numbers 6 to 10 using concrete apparatus.

Group size
Whole class.

What you need
A cassette player, a musical cassette, a hoop between two children, lots of bean bags, a set of large cards, each with a number from 6 to 10 on it, a large space.

What to do
• Space out the hoops well over a large floor area.
• Ask the children to form pairs.
• Put a pile of bean bags in four or five places so that all the children have easy access to them.
• Play some music and ask the children to skip, in their pairs, in and out of the hoops. Stop the music and hold up a number card. Ask each pair to find a hoop and place the correct number of bean bags in it as indicated by the card. Once they have done this, they must sit down beside their hoop.
• Finish the game when one pair is sitting beside their hoop. Ask another pair to count the bean bags to check they have the correct number. Invite the other children to carry on placing the bean bags in their hoops and encourage them to check each other's hoops.
• Ask the children to return the bean bags to their starting point and repeat the game holding up a different number.

Discussion
Encourage the children to work together as a pair. How should they organise themselves? Is it easier if one child stays with the hoop while the other collects the bean bags? Should they count together or one at a time? At first, you can say the number name as you hold it up but after a while, encourage the children to read the number symbol for themselves. Look to see whether any of the pairs have grouped the bean bags systematically to make them easier to count. Point out the importance of this.

Washing line race

Objectives
To reinforce counting numbers 6 to 10, using pictures of objects and to reinforce recognition of the number words.

Group size
Pairs.

What you need
For the preparation: card, felt-tipped pens, scissors, paper, plastic film, paper clips.
For the game: string, pegs, two sets of number word cards (six to ten), picture cards of sets of objects (six to ten), a basket, an egg timer.

Preparation
Make two sets of cards with the number words six to ten on them (two of each). Cover the cards with plastic film. Cut a small slit in each card and attach a paper clip as shown in Figure 1.

Make picture cards of sets of objects (from six to ten), for example, six flowers, eight balls, nine hens, etc. You can draw these using coloured pens, or use rubber stamps, gummed shapes, pictures cut from magazines, etc. Make sure the pictures are in a random arrangement on each card. Cover with plastic film.

What to do
- Fix the string at child height to resemble a washing line. Peg several of the number word cards onto the washing line and place the corresponding picture cards in a basket nearby.
- Ask the players to work together to count the objects on the cards and fix them to the corresponding number word card on the washing line. They should match as many as possible before the sand in the egg timer runs through.
- At the end of the game, ask another child to check the cards. Any wrongly matched cards must be discounted.

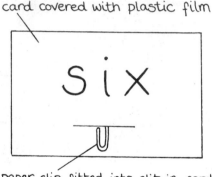

card covered with plastic film

paper clip fitted into slit in card

Figure 1

Discussion
Initially younger children could have extra clues to help them read each word, for example, the number symbol or corresponding spots. Occasionally, ask individuals to explain how they count the random pattern on a card. Do they do it in a logical way? Does their speed and accuracy improve with practice? How many cards can each child match in one minute?

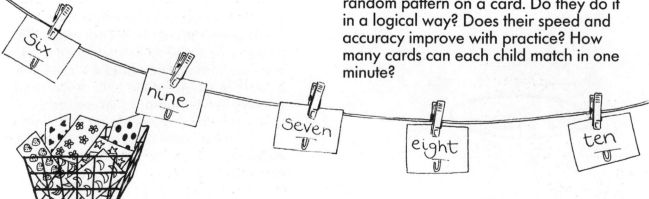

Ordinal numbers

While children may be able to say 'how many' objects there are in a set, they might not fully realise their relative positions in a sequence. They will need a variety of activities to help them appreciate, for example, that 6 comes after 5 but before 7. Simple dot-to-dot pictures, number line games, number rhymes and songs and practical

apparatus such as peg boards and Unifix rods will help foster their understanding.

Similarly, it is important that they can understand and apply words such as first, second, third and fourth in a variety of situations. Using this vocabulary in everyday 'real' situations will help children become familiar with them.

The following games are a useful way of reinforcing ordinal numbers and, once again, they have been organised into two sections — 0 to 5 and 6 to 10. However, it is possible to adapt most of the games to any range of numbers.

Numbers 0 to 5

Doors on houses

Objective
To practise ordering the numbers 1 to 5.

Group size
Two to four.

What you need
For the preparation: a pencil, card, felt-tipped pens, scissors, plastic film.
For the game: base boards, numbered door cards.

Preparation
On the card, draw five simple outlines of houses with equal sized door spaces. Make a photocopy for each child and colour the houses, emphasising the door spaces. Mount on card and cover with film.

Using card, cut out doors to fit the spaces on the houses. Make enough sets, numbered 1 to 5, for each base board. Colour and cover with film.

What to do
• Give each child a base board and spread the door picture cards face down in the middle of the table.
• Ask each player to take turns to choose a door picture card and place it on a house in the correct position. If a player already has that door, she must return it, face downwards.
• Finish the game when one player has placed all the doors on her houses in the correct order.

Discussion
Do the children need number 4? Does it come before or after number 3? Which numbers do they still need to find?

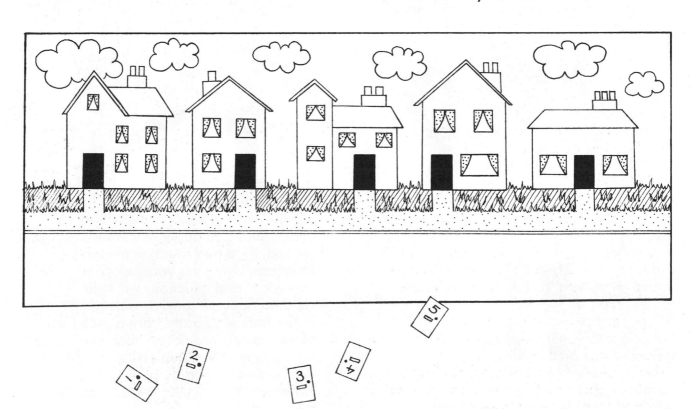

Ships

Objective
To recognise ordinal number symbols.

Group size
Pairs.

What you need
For the preparation: glue, card, felt-tipped pens, plastic film, scissors, a die. For the game: a colour die, base boards, matching coloured pieces of card, ordering strips.

Preparation
Draw a large simple outline of a ship and photocopy it. Colour each section of the ship differently. Mount on card and cover with film.

Make coloured pieces of card to match perfectly the different sections of the ships. Cover with film.

Make ordering strips on card to show the order of coloured pieces of card which have to be added to the ships. Make several strips with colours in a different order on each.

Make a colour die by sticking circles of different colours (to match colours on ship) to each face. Make sure that one face has a white circle.

What to do
● Give each player a base board and place the matching coloured pieces in the middle of the table.
● Ask each player to choose an ordering strip. Explain that the strip shows the order of coloured pieces which have to be added to the ship.
● Let each player take turns to throw the colour die until it shows the colour indicated first on their ordering strip. When a player rolls that colour he must take the corresponding coloured piece of ship and place it on his base board.

● Encourage the players to continue throwing the die until it shows the second colour and so on.
● If the die shows a colour which a player has already covered, no action needs to be taken. If the die shows white, let the player have the next colour indicated on his strip.
● Let the game continue until one player has completely covered his ship in the order indicated on the strip.

Discussion
Which colour are the children trying to throw on the die? Which position is it on their ordering strip? Is red in the same position on two of the ordering strips?

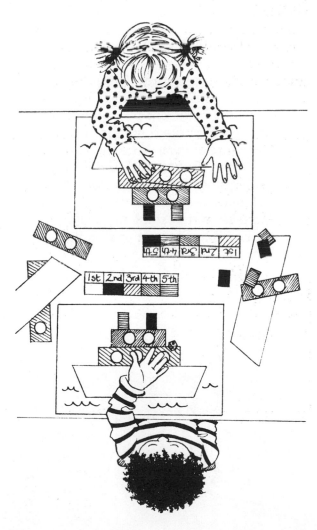

Numbers 6 to 10

Shopping game

Objective
To practise ordering the numbers 6 to 10.

Group size
Pairs.

What you need
For the preparation: glue, felt-tipped pens, card, plastic film.
For the game: base boards, a number die, picture and number cards, two counters.

Preparation
On card, draw a large simple route and add two starting squares. Draw ten shops at various points on the board, making the main part of the shop large enough to hold a card. Write a number from 6 to 10 on each roof (two of each). Colour some random squares red and the squares leading to each shop another colour. Cover with film.
　　Make a set of ten small picture and number cards to fit the shops on the board. Cover with film.

What to do
• Place a base board between the players and ask them to put their counters on a starting square, either the same or different ones.
• Place the small picture cards on the shops to match the numbers on their roofs.
• Invite each player to take turns to throw the die and move her counter the number of squares indicated, either forwards or backwards. The player may choose any route but she must visit the shops in order, starting with 6. The player does not need to throw an exact number to reach a shop.
• Once a player has visited a shop, she must collect the small picture card and place it in front of her. Let the players continue collecting the cards and placing them in the correct sequence.
• Explain that if a player lands on a red 'Go faster' square, she can move immediately to the next shop and collect her card. Once a card has been removed from a shop, the other player must go to the second shop of that number.
• Let the game continue until one player has collected all five cards and displayed them in the correct order.

Discussion
Encourage the children to talk about which number they need to reach next. What number do they need to throw to land on the next red 'Go faster' square? How many more numbers do they need to collect to reach 10?

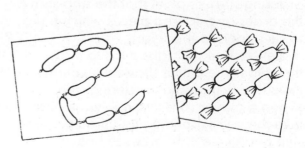

first second third fourth

The flower pot game

Objective
To recognise the ordinal words from first to tenth.

Group size
Pairs.

What you need
For the preparation: felt-tipped pens, plastic film, scissors.
For the game: base boards, card flowers, word cards.

Preparation
On card, draw ten simple flower pot shapes, making sure there is adequate space above for card flowers. Photocopy and mount on card. Colour the pots and cover with film.

Using card, make two sets of ten differently coloured flowers and two sets of ordinal word cards (first to tenth). All sets of cards must fit the flower pots on the base board.

What to do
• Give each player a base board and place the card flowers in a pile. Put the small ordinal word cards face down in a pile.
• Let each player take turns to pick up a word card, take a card flower from the top of the pile and place it in the flower pot indicated on the word card. He must then put the word card on the bottom of the flower pot.
• If a player picks a card which he does not need, he must return it to the bottom of the pile.
• Continue the game until one player has placed a flower on each of his ten flower pots.

Discussion
At first, you could use a chinagraph pencil to write the ordinal words on each flower pot so the children can match word to word. At the end of the game, ask specific questions. Where is the red flower? What colour flower is in the eighth flower pot? Which flower pot comes before or after the blue flower?

Conservation of numbers to 10

A child may be able to count five bricks easily, but if they are rearranged into a different pattern problems may arise, particularly if the bricks appear to occupy far more space. Sometimes children may be able to conserve small numbers of objects (up to five) but find larger numbers far more difficult. It can be useful for them to compare two sets of objects having the same number of members. By matching, rearranging one set and matching again, the child will slowly realise that the total number in the set remains constant.

Acquiring the concept of conservation can be aided through a wide range of practical activities. The games outlined below provide opportunities to explore this concept. Although the first two games are designed to reinforce specific numbers, they can easily be adapted to other numbers.

Robot buttons

Objective
To investigate patterns of four with concrete apparatus.

Group size
Pairs.

What you need
Photocopiable page 94, counters or Unifix cubes, one die with three faces labelled '4' and three faces labelled '0'.

What to do
● Give each child a base board and a pile of counters (or Unifix cubes).
● Let each player take turns to throw the die. If he throws a 0 no action is taken. If he throws a 4, he must take four counters from the pile and place them in the squares on one of his robot control panels. Explain that only one counter in each square is allowed.
● The next time a 4 is thrown on the die, the player must try to place four more counters on the second robot's control panel in a different pattern.
● Continue the game until one child has filled all the robot control panels with different patterns of four.

Discussion
Encourage the children to devise their own arrangements of the counters rather than copy each other. Initially, it may take some time for them to look carefully at any arrangements already made on their robots to avoid duplication. Once the game is finished, invite the players to compare patterns and discuss any differences or similarities.

Patterns of 7 walk

Objective
To identify patterns of seven.

Group size
Two to four.

What you need
For the preparation: card, felt-tipped pens, plastic film, coloured chinagraph pens.
For the game: a base board, small plastic figures (one for each player), five counters of the same colour for each player, a number die.

Preparation

Draw a large simple route map on card and label the start and finish squares. Colour five squares red at random along the route. Cover with plastic film.

Using the chinagraph pens (so that the game can be adapted for other numbers), draw two sets of pictures beside each red square — one which illustrates 7 and one which does not.

What to do

• Give each group of players a base board. Place it so that all players can reach it easily. Ask each player to choose a small figure to act as a counter and five counters of the same colour.
• From the starting point, the players must take turns to throw the die which indicates the number of squares they can move along the track.
• Explain that when a player reaches a red square, she must stop, no matter what number was shown on the die. She must then look at the two groups of nearby pictures carefully and mark the one which illustrates a set of seven by placing a coloured counter on it.
• Finish the game when one player reaches the end of the track and has marked all the pictures correctly.
• If some of the pictures have not been marked correctly, let the game continue until another player is successful.

Discussion

Encourage each child to look for the patterns of seven individually rather than automatically copying the previous player. At the end of the game, look at each of the pictures in turn to determine which one has a pattern of seven. Once this has been established, count how many players had correctly marked each one.

Fill the stocking

Objective

To extend conservation of numbers 5 to 10.

Group size

Two to four.

What you need

For the preparation: card, scissors, felt-tipped pens, plastic film.
For the game: base boards, number cards, picture cards.

Preparation

Cut a large stocking shape from card. Draw a large square on the toe and a two by three grid on the vertical part of the stocking, making sure each square is large enough to hold a card. Cover with film.

Make a set of number cards (5 to 10) and sets of six picture cards for each number, with the pictures arranged in different patterns. All the cards must fit the squares on the base board.

What to do

• Give each player a base board and allow them to choose a number card which they must place in the square on the toe of the stocking. Explain that their stocking will only hold pictures of objects with patterns of that particular number.

Addition to 10

It can take a surprisingly long time for children to understand number bonds up to ten and even longer for them to be able to instantly recall them. A good foundation can only be built upon a wide variety of concrete experiences.

At first, it may be helpful to restrict the numbers which the children are handling to five or less but gradually larger numbers can be introduced. Many commercially-produced games omit the use of zero but this can be rectified in home-made games by consciously including zero.

Initially, recording will either be very simple ('4 and 3 together make') or it will take the form of a discussion between teacher and child. The introduction of more formal symbols (+ and =) is not wise until the child has experienced a range of practical activities.

'Counting on' with number strips is another essential experience which helps a child to understand addition. Games which use a numbered track are an enjoyable way of introducing and reinforcing this skill.

The following games provide an opportunity for practising number bonds in a more relaxed games situation. They should only be introduced after a wide variety of practical experiences and a great deal of discussion.

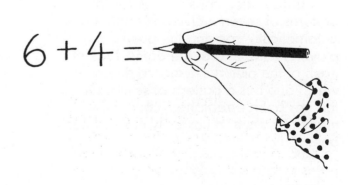

- Shuffle the small picture cards and spread them out face downwards.
- Let each player take turns to pick one of the cards. Explain that if it illustrates a pattern of objects for the number she is collecting, she must place it on the stocking. If not, she must return it face down.
- Continue the game until one child has covered all of the squares on her stocking.

Discussion

Suggest that the players say which number each card illustrates as they pick it up. Occasionally, stop the game and ask the players how many more cards they need to finish their stocking. At the end of the game, invite the players to describe some of the arrangements of the objects.

Wheels on the bus

Objective
To experience finding combinations of numbers which add up to six.

Group size
Two to four.

What you need
For the preparation: card, felt-tipped pens, plastic film, glue.
For the game: base boards, counters, a number die.

Preparation
Draw a simple outline of a bus without wheels and make enough photocopies for each player to have four. Draw a different number of wheels on each bus, from 0 to 5, making sure the wheels are roughly the same size as the counters. Colour and mount on card. Cover with film.

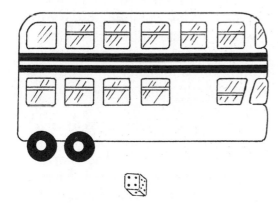

What to do
● Shuffle the bus cards and give each player four. Explain that each bus needs to have six wheels altogether and ask the players to look carefully at each of their buses to find out how many wheels they already have.

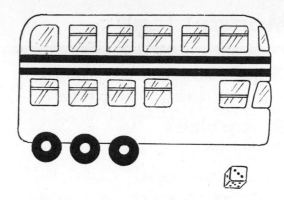

● Let each player take turns to throw the die. Explain that if the number shown would complete the set of six wheels on one of their buses, they can collect that number of counters and place them as wheels. If they do not need that number or they already have it, no action is taken and the turn passes to the next player.
● Continue until one player has all six wheels for each of his buses.

Discussion
Which number do the children need to throw on the die? Do any of them need the same number? How many more buses do they need to complete? Is the number they have thrown too many or not enough? Make sure they realise that each combination of numbers should always have a total of six. At the end of the game, can the children say how many different combinations they have found for making six?

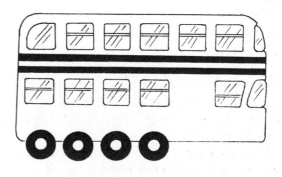

Monster legs

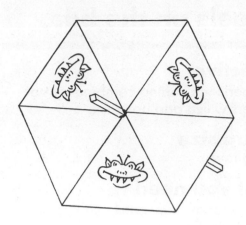

Objective
To practise adding totals up to ten.

Group size
Two to four.

What you need
For the preparation: card, scissors, felt-tipped pens, plastic film, a used matchstick.
For the game: monster cards, numbered cave cards, a monster spinner, Unifix cubes.

Preparation
For the monster cards, draw a simple outline of a monster without legs and photocopy it several times. On each copy, draw legs at the back and front of the monster, using different numbers (from 0 to 5) so that you cover all combinations of number bonds up to ten, for example, $1+3=4$ and $2+2=4$. Colour and mount on card. Cover with film and cut each monster in half.

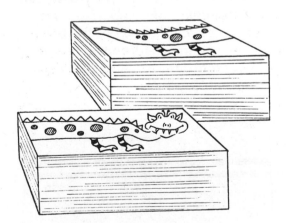

To make the cave cards, draw a large outline of a cave and photocopy it eleven times. Number each from 0 to 10. Colour, mount on card and cover with film.

To make a monster spinner, cut a hexagon from strong card and divide into six sections. Draw a monster head on every other section. Cover in film and secure a used matchstick through the middle.

What to do
• Place the monster cards face down in two piles – heads in one, tails in the other. Ask the children to order the cave pictures in a line from 0 to 10 and put ten pieces of Unifix on top of each cave.
• Explain that the number of legs on each whole monster indicates the number of the cave where he lives and that if the children return a monster to his cave, he will reward them with one piece of 'treasure' (a Unifix cube).
• Ask each child to take turns to spin the monster spinner. If it lands on a monster face, they can pick up one monster 'head' card and one 'tail' card. If not, the spinner is passed to the next player. When they have the 'head' and 'tail' cards, they should count the total number of legs and place the monster on the cave with the corresponding number. They can then take one piece of 'treasure'.
• Continue the game until one child has collected three pieces of 'treasure' (or more if their concentration span is long enough).

Discussion

Encourage the children to 'count on'. For example, if the child can instantly recognise the total number of legs on the 'head' card as three, they can start at three when counting on the remaining legs. Is there more than one monster in any of the caves? If there are, discuss the different combinations of legs. Can the children predict which caves are more likely to have more monsters in them and say why?

Caterpillar crawl

Objective

To reinforce counting on using a picture number strip.

Group size

Pairs.

What you need

For the preparation: card, felt-tipped pens, scissors, plastic film.
For the game: butterfly cards, caterpillar cards, a numbered leaf track, 'start at' and 'crawl on' cards.

Preparation

To make the leaf track, draw eleven large leaves on card and colour in. Number them from 0 to 10. Cover with film.

On small pieces of card, write 'start at' and 'crawl on', followed by numbers from 0 to 5. Cover with film.

On card, draw and cut out twelve caterpillars. Colour six yellow and six red. Cover with film.

On six small cards, draw and colour a butterfly. Cover with film.

What to do

● Place the leaf track in between the two players. Give one player the yellow caterpillars and the other the red caterpillars.
● Mix the butterfly cards with the 'start at' cards and place them face down in a pile. Place the 'crawl on' cards face down in a separate pile.
● Each player must take turns to pick a 'start at' card and a 'crawl on' card and use these instructions to place his caterpillar on a leaf. If another caterpillar is already on the leaf, the player must remove his caterpillar and re-use it at his next turn. If a butterfly card is picked, this turns the caterpillar into a butterfly which does not need a leaf to eat. The player has to miss a turn and place his caterpillar on the butterfly card.
● Continue the game until one player has placed all his caterpillars on leaves or had them turned into butterflies. The winner is the child with the most caterpillars on the leaves.

Discussion

Make sure the players realise that they do not count the leaf which they 'start at' when they 'crawl on'. Can the children predict which number leaf they will land on? Encourage them to count how many caterpillars they have managed to place and say how many more they have left.

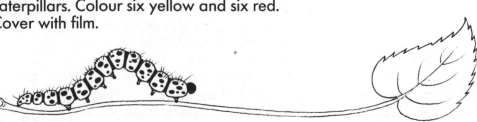

Subtraction of numbers to 10

As with addition, subtraction also needs to be firmly rooted in practical activities. The introduction of abstract signs and symbols (− and =) is best left until the children have had plenty of experience using concrete materials.

As well as 'taking away', children also need to 'find the difference' by matching and comparing two sets. This is sometimes a more difficult concept to acquire because it is less common in everyday situations and thus more unfamiliar.

At this stage, complicated recording is not necessary. Simple games like the following can help reinforce the idea of subtraction once the children have experienced a wide variety of practical activities.

Five brown teddies

Objective
To reinforce the idea of 'take away' using concrete materials.

Group size
A small group or the whole class.

What you need
Five brown teddies, small cardboard boxes, sticky labels.

What to do
● Teach the children the following song to the tune of 'Ten green bottles':

> Five brown teddies sitting on a wall,
> Five brown teddies sitting on a wall,
> And if one brown teddy should accidentally fall,
> There'd be four brown teddies sitting on the wall.
>
> Four brown teddies sitting on a wall, etc.

Continue until there are no teddies sitting on the wall.
● Once the children are familiar with the tune and the words, use real teddy bears on a cardboard box wall to accompany the song. Number each bear using sticky labels. Ask five children to stand behind the teddies and knock one down when indicated in the song.

Discussion
Make sure the children understand the order in which the bears should be knocked down. Should number five or number one be first? Can the children explain what is happening to the numbers as the song progresses? Choose

individuals to knock down a specific number of bears and to describe what has happened. Introduce the terminology for subtraction. Allow the children to specify how many bears are to be knocked down and to choose someone to describe the subtraction number sentence.

Subtraction lotto

Objective
To reinforce 'take away' in a pictorial form.

Group size
Two to four.

What you need
For the preparation: card, a black pen, plastic film.
For the game: base boards, picture cards.

Preparation
Make a set of small picture cards of, for example, simple items to eat, including red crosses to indicate take away. The cards should fit the squares of the base board.

Draw a three by three grid on card and write in each square the answer to a subtraction number sentence illustrated on the small picture cards. Cover with plastic film. Make each base board different.

What to do
• Before playing, make sure the children understand that the X on the picture cards means the objects have been taken away from the set.
• Give each player a base board and spread the small cards face down in the middle of the table.
• Ask each player to take turns to pick a card and read the 'take away' picture on

it. For example, 'two sweets take away one sweet leaves one sweet'. If she has 1 on her base board, she must place the picture card on top of it. If not, she must return it to the middle of the table.
• Continue the game until one player has covered her base board with pictures.

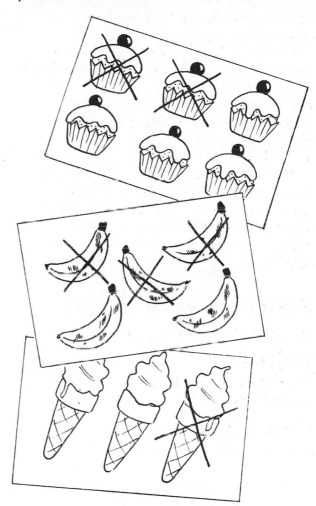

Discussion
During the game, ask the children to make up stories to explain the cards. For example, 'I had three lollies and they all melted, so there were zero left'. At the end of the game, ask how many more cards each player needed. Allow them to complete their boards. Are there any cards which could belong to more than one board?

Find the difference

Objective
To reinforce 'find the difference' using numbers to ten.

Group size
Two to four.

What you need
For the preparation: card, felt-tipped pens, plastic film.
For the game: ten number strips for each player, used matchsticks, counters.

Preparation
Cut twenty (or forty) equal sized strips of card. Draw (or rubber stamp) different numbers of objects on each strip, making sure they are evenly spaced. Colour and cover with film.

What to do
● Place all the strips face down in the middle of the table with the matchsticks and counters.

● Ask the players to take turns to pick up two strips and place them one above the other. They must then use matchsticks to match the members of one set with the other to find the difference. Having established the difference between the two sets, they should collect that number of counters and return the cards.
● Continue the game until one player has collected ten counters.

Discussion
Before playing, make sure the players understand how to place the number strips one underneath the other and match the sets using matchsticks. At the end of the game, ask the players to compare their counters with each other and find the difference in their scores. After a while, some children may not need the help of matchsticks.

Patterns

Chapter six

Patterns can be seen everywhere, on natural and man-made structures. However, not all children will be aware of them and some will need help to recognise the regularity and repetition which is the essence of all patterns. Patterns are a theme that appears in many areas of the curriculum, from P.E. to music and from science to art.

Being able to recognise a pattern and use this knowledge to make predictions is an important mathematical skill. With early years pupils, patterns are most likely to be explored in colour, shape, size, position and early number. Practical activities, such as copying and continuing colour patterns with beads or shape patterns with bricks, are very important in helping children to recognise and predict patterns.

The games in this chapter are intended to help further children's development in this area.

Dress the snowman

Objective
To recognise and name some common patterns.

Group size
Four.

What to do
• Give each player a base board. Shuffle the card clothing and give each player one of each item.
• Using a shoe box, for example, ask each player to place his items of clothing in it, so that the players can't see each other's items.
• Invite each player to take turns and ask any other player for an item of card clothing in his particular pattern. If the player has it, she must hand it over to be placed in the correct position on the base board.

• Any player obtaining an item of clothing can have a second turn. If the player is unlucky, the turn passes to the next player.
• Continue the game until one player has a fully dressed snowman.

What you need
For the preparation: card, glue, felt-tipped pens, plastic film, scissors.
For the game: base boards, sets of clothing, shoe boxes.

Preparation
For the base board, draw a simple outline of a snowman and photocopy it for each player. Draw a belt on each in a different pattern and colour. Mount on card and cover with film.
    For the snowman's clothes, draw and cut out items of clothing, such as a hat, scarf, gloves and buttons. Fill each set with the same patterns as on the snowman's belts. Cover with film.

Discussion
Before the game, make sure the children can name and identify each pattern. Can they find other examples of a similar pattern in the room? What do we call something without a pattern? As the game progresses, ask the children to name the items of clothing which they still need.

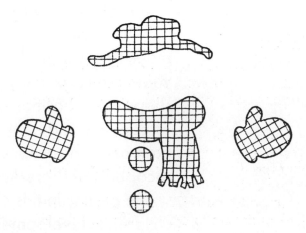

Print a scarf

Objective
To create and continue a shape pattern.

Group size
Pairs.

What you need
Different colours and lengths of oblong-shaped sugar paper, water-based paints, junk materials for printing (cotton reels, pieces of balsa, corks, wooden bricks and cardboard tubes), printing trays, glue, odd pieces of paper or wool.

pattern on half of each row on their scarf. Younger children may need the half-way line to be marked so they know where to stop. Emphasise that they must only print one shape in each square.
● When both children have finished their half, ask them to swap over and continue each pattern to the end of the scarf.
● Once they have both finished, let each child check that the other child has completed the pattern correctly.
● When the prints are dry, ask the children to add a paper or wool fringing at each end to complete the scarf.

What to do
● Ask the children to help you divide each of the oblong-shaped pieces of sugar paper into a grid. Young children may need guidance.
● Allow each child to choose the colour and length of their paper and explain that this is to be a scarf decorated with interesting patterns.
● In pairs, the children should use the junk materials to print a different shape

Discussion
While the children are working, encourage them to think of different shape patterns and to increase their complexity. As they continue the patterns, encourage them to check continually the original sequence to make sure they achieve the correct pattern. Can they identify any mistakes and say what has gone wrong? Ask them to spot the most complicated pattern and predict what should come next.

Beach ball patterns

Objective
To copy and continue simple number patterns with practical apparatus.

Group size
Pairs.

What you need
For the preparation: card, scissors, felt-tipped pens, plastic film.
For the game: base boards, a die with three faces labelled 4 and three labelled 5, counters, number sequence cards.

Preparation
For each base board, cut a circle from card. Draw two lines across the middle to separate a plain section, large enough for a sequence of counters to fit on. Colour and decorate the top and bottom sections of the circle. Cover with film.

Make several number sequence cards such as 4, 5, 5, 4, 5, 5.

Label a die, three faces with the number 4 and three faces with the number 5.

What to do
● Give each player a base board and a pile of counters between them.

● Ask each player to choose a number sequence card. Explain that they should use the counters to make a pattern from left to right in the middle section of their beach ball, following the number sequence shown on the card (see Figure 1).

Figure 1

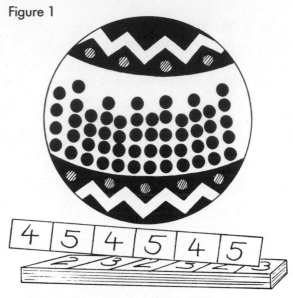

● Invite each player to take turns to throw the die. If they throw the number at the beginning of their sequence card, the player must place that number of counters vertically on the far left side of her beach ball. If not, she must pass the die to the next player.
● Ask them to place the counters on their beach ball whenever they throw the next number in their sequence. Initially, children may use the number sequence card as a reference but they must learn to continue the sequence themselves.
● Let them play until one child has correctly covered the middle section of her beach ball.

Discussion
Encourage the children to remember the number sequence and not rely on the number sequence card. Have any of them deliberately included a colour sequence in their pattern?

Measures

Chapter seven

Measures is an umbrella term which covers several mathematical areas such as length, time, money and capacity. Early years pupils will experience all of these areas incidentally as they play, for example, finding the correct sized clothes for a particular doll and filling containers with sand. However, you may notice that as they play, many will use words such as 'big' indiscriminately, applying it to height, weight and length. It is important to teach them the correct terminology when making comparisons.

Games are often an ideal means of reinforcing a specific aspect of mathematics. In this chapter, a section has been devoted to each of the following — length, time, money and capacity.

Length

Opportunities for discussing length can arise in many play situations such as building roadways with bricks, constructing fences in the toy farm and joining carriages to trains. Sensitive questioning will refine a child's use of vocabulary such as 'longer than', 'shorter than', 'longest' and 'as long as'.

Once they have mastered comparative vocabulary, children can be introduced to measuring using non-standard units. As well as rigid objects, let them use flexible objects such as string to help develop the concept of conservation.

There are many practical problems when using non-standard units to measure with. Children may not be aware that any objects to be compared need to be positioned properly and the ends of each item need to be level. Similarly, they may not realise that each unit needs to be placed end-to-end leaving no gaps.

Once the children have had plenty of practical experience, it is important to encourage them to estimate before measuring. Even if their initial guesses are wildly inaccurate, they will gradually improve with practice.

The following games can support and extend the practical measuring activities which are essential for a sound foundation in this area.

68

The crocodile game

Objectives
To experience the term 'as long as' and practise the correct positioning for accurate measuring.

Group size
Three.

What you need
For the preparation: card, felt-tipped pens, scissors, sticky tape, plastic film, three cardboard tubes of different lengths, brown paper.
For the game: a base board, three card logs, nine card crocodiles.

Preparation
On a large piece of card, draw a river with grassy banks at the top and bottom. Cover with film and cut nine slits in the river. These should be large enough for the crocodiles to slip in and out easily. If necessary, reinforce the slits with sticky tape.

For the card logs, use one small, one medium and one large cardboard tube. Cover each with brown paper and stick a card circle on each end.

For the crocodiles, draw three small, three large and three medium ones on card. They should be the equivalent lengths of the logs. Colour, cut out and cover in film.

What to do
● Without the children watching, push the crocodiles into the slits in the base board and place it in the middle of the table.
● Let each child choose a log and explain that they should try to find three crocodiles which are exactly the same length as their log.
● Ask each child in turn to choose a crocodile, slide it out from the base

board and compare it with their log. If it is as long as the log, the child can keep it. If not, the crocodile must be returned to the base board.
● Let the game continue until one child has collected all three of her crocodiles.

Discussion
Make sure the children place the end of the crocodile level with the end of the log and explain why this is important. Before placing the crocodile beside the log, ask the children to predict whether they think the crocodile is as long as their log. At the end of the game, discuss how many more crocodiles the other players needed. Suggest that they order the crocodiles according to length.

T-shirts on the line

Objective
To experience using non-standard units for measuring.

Group size
Two to four.

What you need
For the preparation: card, felt-tipped pens, scissors, plastic film.
For the game: base boards, card t-shirts, a die numbered 1, 2 and 3 (twice each).

Preparation
To make the base boards, draw a simple washing line between two posts. Each line should differ in length by one card t-shirt. Mount on card and cover in film.

Draw, colour and cut out enough identically sized card t-shirts to fill each base board. Cover with film.

Make a game die, numbered 1, 2 and 3 each on two faces.

What to do
● Turn the base boards upside down and hold them in a fan shape to conceal their length. Ask each player to choose one and turn it over.

- Spread out the card t-shirts.
- Ask each player in turn to throw the die and pick up that number of t-shirts. She must then put the t-shirts on the washing line starting at the left-hand side and working towards the right. Each t-shirt must touch the previous one with no gaps.
- Let the game continue until one player has a full washing line of t-shirts, finishing with the exact number shown on the die.

Discussion

Ask the children to compare the length of their washing lines. Who has the longest/shortest line? Can they estimate how many t-shirts will fill their line? At the end of the game, ask the runners-up how many more t-shirts they think they need. Let them check. Count the t-shirts on each washing line and compare with the original estimate. Ask them to put the washing lines in order according to the number of t-shirts. Which washing line has the most/least number of t-shirts?

71

Mice tails

Objective
To experience the terms 'longer than' and 'shorter than' and develop an understanding of conservation.

Group size
Two to four.

What you need
For the preparation: card, string, felt-tipped pens, a hole punch, scissors, plastic film.
For the game: twelve (or more for four players) mice cards, string, a colour die.

Preparation
Draw a large simple outline of a mouse and make eleven photocopies. Colour two mice in each of the following colours: red, blue, yellow, green, orange and brown. Cut them out, mount on card and cover with film. Punch a hole at the tail end and tie a different length of string on each one.

Make a colour die showing the six colours used for the mice cards.

What to do
● Invite the children to spread the mice cards face upwards on the table with their tails in a variety of curled shapes.
● Ask each one to choose a piece of string.
● Let each player take turns to throw the colour die. The player can then choose a mouse of the colour thrown. Before moving the mouse, she must say whether its string tail is longer or shorter than her piece of string. She should then compare the two pieces of string. If she was right, let her keep the mouse. If not, she must return the mouse.
● Continue the game until one player has collected an agreed number of mice.

Discussion
Encourage the children to use the correct vocabulary. Make sure they understand that they should compare the length of the tails only and not include the body. Also check that they place the tails in the correct position before measuring. Is it difficult or easy to tell whether the mouse tail is longer or shorter? At the end of the game, ask the children to place the mice in order according to the length of their tail.

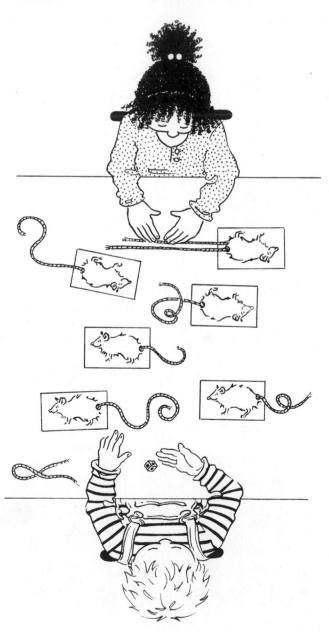

Time

The abstract concept of time is extremely difficult for young children to grasp. The regular, routine activities in the early years classroom may help very young children begin to realise that some events happen at specific times and that there is a sequence to the day. It is important to enlarge their vocabulary of time words. Discussion about their daily activities will help the children to relate such words to their own lives.

The majority of children come into contact with a wide variety of clocks although it may take a long time before they can tell the time and even longer to understand what it means. With early years pupils, encourage them to look in

detail at the clock face, to notice the difference in the length of the hands and watch them moving round. Older children may recognise the sequence of numbers around a clock face and may be capable of learning to read the 'o'clocks'.

Understanding the concept of the passage of time will develop slowly over a period of many years but activities using a variety of timers will help children work towards this.

The following games need to be introduced carefully to match the child's stage of development. For example, to benefit from doing the clock puzzles, children need to have looked at a variety of clock faces and to be familiar with numbers.

What's the time, Mr Wolf?

Objective
To reinforce 'o'clocks'.

Group size
Whole class.

What you need
For the preparation: card, felt-tipped pens, scissors, stapler.
For the game: a toy clock with a large face, a wolf's headdress, a large space, a chair.

Preparation
Make the wolf's headdress by attaching card ears to a card headband that will fit the average-sized child's head.

What to do
● Place the clock on a chair in the middle of the playing area. Choose one child to be Mr (or Mrs) Wolf and ask him to wear the headdress.
● Explain that the other children are the lambs and ask them to stand at one end of the area.
● Ask the lambs to chant, 'What's the time, Mr Wolf?' Mr Wolf must set the hands on the clock to any o'clock he chooses. The lambs have to say the time shown.
● If Mr Wolf sets the hands to 1 o'clock, the lambs must shout, 'Dinner time'. They must try to run past Mr Wolf and touch the wall at the opposite end. Mr Wolf should try to catch one of them; if he succeeds, ask them to swap places but if not, the lambs must return to their starting point. There is no time limit for the game.

Discussion
Before playing the game, make sure the children realise which are the long and short hands on the clock. Practise a few 'o'clocks' to give them confidence in reading the time.

Clock puzzles

Objectives
To recognise number sequence on a clock face and to focus on the passage of time.

Group size
Pairs.

What you need
For the preparation: card, felt-tipped pens, scissors, plastic film.
For the game: five clock puzzles, a sand timer (appropriate to ability).

Preparation
Draw five large clocks on card. Colour and cover with film. Cut each one into twelve pieces.

What to do
● Invite the children to choose one clock puzzle each and spread out the pieces, picture side up.
● Challenge them to complete their clock puzzles before the sand runs through the egg timer.

Discussion
At the end of the game, discuss their efforts with the children. How much of the puzzle have they managed to do? How many more pieces were left? Invite the children to complete any puzzles not yet finished. Are all the numbers in the correct sequence? Suggest that they check each other's puzzle. If there are any incorrectly placed pieces, can they reposition them properly? Can they read the time on the clock? What sort of clock is it?

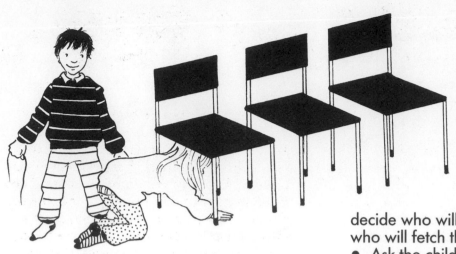

Water clock race

Objective
To appreciate the passage of time.

Group size
Four.

What you need
For the preparation: an empty yoghurt pot, a jam jar, Plasticine, a skewer.
For the game: a water clock, water, a tunnel made from large chairs (one per pair), beads, laces.

Preparation
Make a hole in the bottom of a yoghurt pot and wedge it firmly with Plasticine into the top of a large jam jar.

What to do
• Place the water clock on a table or chair and show the children how to operate it.
• Ask the children to form pairs and decide who will thread the beads and who will fetch them.
• Ask the child with the lace to stand at one end of the tunnel and place a box of beads at the other. Explain that the second child must crawl through the tunnel and fetch one bead at a time for her partner who must then thread it onto the lace.
• Set the water clock going by filling the yoghurt pot with water. Stop the game when all the water has run through.
• Ask the children to compare the number of beads threaded on each lace to see which pair has won.

Discussion
Before the game starts, suggest that the children estimate how many beads they think they will be able to thread. Did they manage to guess correctly? What is the difference between the two sets of beads?

NB: This game can also be played with other types of timers.

Money

Most early years pupils will be familiar with money although they may not necessarily be able to recognise and name each coin or understand its value. Organise a trip to a local shop. As a follow-up, a pretend shop would provide essential role-play experience as well as establishing how much the children understand about exchanging goods for money. The process of swapping money for goods gives valuable experience even if the rate of exchange is rather haphazard. Price tags need not reflect the real value of objects, but use numbers within the children's experience.

It is important to show children real money but it may not be feasible to use real coins all the time. Facsimile coins can be used but they should be exact replicas of each coin and not simply a token with a value stamped on. Always make sure the children connect each cardboard or plastic coin with its real counterpart. Sticky paper coins and rubber stamps may also be useful for making games and workcards.

The following games should only be introduced to pupils after they have had plenty of practical experience of handling money.

Money bug

Objective
To practise recognising coins.

Group size
Two to four.

What you need
Photocopiable page 95, a collection of six different coins, one die labelled with the value of each coin.

What to do
● Give each child a copy of photocopiable page 95 and place the coins in the middle of the table.
● Ask each child to take turns to throw the die. He should then find the coin which corresponds to the value shown and place it on top of the same coin on the money bug.
● If the child has covered all the coins shown by the die, the next player has a turn.

● Let them play until one child has covered all the coins shown on his money bug.

Discussion
Talk about the different coins shown on the money bug. How many 1p coins are shown? Where is the 50p coin? Are the coins the same on both sides? Which coins are the same size, colour or shape? How many more coins does each child need?

Filling up purses

Objective
To experience exchanging 1p coins for a 5p coin.

Group size
Two to four.

What you need
A purse for each child, three sets of number cards (0 to 5), 1p and 5p coins.

What to do
● Ask each child to choose a purse. Place the number cards face down in a pile. Put the coins in separate containers within easy reach of all the children.
● Let each child take turns to pick a card from the top of the pile and collect the corresponding number of 1p coins. The child must place the coins in front of her and when she has collected five 1p coins, she can exchange them for one 5p piece which she must put in her purse. She can keep any remaining 1p coins until she has enough for another 5p coin.
● Let the game continue until one child has five 5p coins, or a different number, according to the children's ability.

Discussion
Point out the similarities and differences between the two coins. Make sure the children realise that five 1p coins have the same value as a 5p coin. If the children can count in fives, encourage them to count the total value of the coins in their purses. Can they suggest ways in which their 5p coins could be exchanged for other coins, 10p or 20p?

Toy shop

Objective
To experience matching coins to a given total value.

Group size
Two to four.

What you need
For the preparation: card, sticky paper coins, felt-tipped pens, plastic film.
For the game: a base board, a collection of coins, a number die, counters, six toy cards, six toys (as on the cards).

Preparation
Use a variety of sticky paper coins to form a circuit on card. Cover with film.

Make simple drawings of six different toys on six equal sized cards. Label each toy with a price tag under 50p or £1, according to the children's ability.

What to do
• Place the toy cards face down on the table. Ask each child to choose a toy card, look at it without the others seeing, and place it, face down, in front of them. Put the coins and the base board within their reach.
• Ask them to place their counter at any point on the track.
• Let each child take turns to throw the die and move their counter along the track according to the number thrown, either backwards or forwards. The child must then collect whatever coin the counter lands on and put it towards the total cost of the toy on their card. If the coin exceeds the cost shown, the child does not have to take it.
• Continue the game until one child can buy the toy on their card with the exact money.

Discussion
Keep reminding the children of the total value which they are trying to achieve so that they are not tempted to collect coins randomly. Encourage them to group the coins into sets to make counting easier. Ask them questions such as, how much more money do you need? Which coins could match this amount? If you collect a 50p, will it be more than you need? At the end of the game, invite each child to count how much money they have and compare it with how much they needed. Can they find the coins to make up the difference?

Capacity

Capacity should be introduced to early years pupils in practical ways. Water and sand play provides essential experience for later concepts. Other pouring materials, such as rice or lentils, can also provide interesting variations. Offer a wide range of containers which differ in size and shape. Initially, young children need plenty of practice to develop enough hand—eye co-ordination to pour from one container to another without spilling. Essential vocabulary such as 'full', 'half full', 'empty', 'holds more' and 'holds less' can be introduced naturally as the children play. With experience, they will

gradually notice that many pouring materials take the shape of the container.

Eventually, you can introduce measuring with non-standard units. Activities can be extended by using larger filling materials such as dried peas, small bricks, fir cones and marbles. As they play, children will notice that some of these materials leave spaces and do not take the shape of the container as well as the pouring materials. They may also appreciate that some containers will hold more than others.

The following games should only be introduced to pupils who have had a broad experience of play activities involving sand, water and so on.

Magic potions

half full

Objective
To reinforce terms such as 'full', 'half full' and 'empty'.

full

Group size
Three.

What you need
For the preparation: card, felt-tipped pens, plastic film.
For the game: three base boards, a set of fifteen small cards.

Preparation
Using three equal-sized pieces of card, draw a shelf on two of them with 'full' written on one and 'half full' on the other. On the third card, draw a dustbin and the word 'empty'. Make fifteen small picture cards, five each illustrating 'full', 'half full' and 'empty'. They should be small enough so that five cards will fit on each base board. Cover cards and base boards with plastic film.

What to do
● Before starting the game, make sure the children understand the terms 'full', 'half full' and 'empty'.

● Turn the base boards face down and ask the children to choose one each.
● Spread out the small cards face down.
● Explain that the children have to sort out the witch's magic potions and put them in the correct place. Make sure they understand which ones to collect.
● Let each player take turns to pick a card. If it belongs to their board they keep it. If not, they return it upside down.
● Let the game continue until one player has collected five correct cards.

Discussion
During the game, encourage the children to use the appropriate vocabulary. At the end of the game, ask the players how many more cards they needed. Can they

empty

find their missing cards from those remaining? Can they find each set of cards showing the same container and then order the three cards from 'empty' to 'full'?

Sand-castles

Objective
To experience the concept 'holds more' (or 'holds less').

Group size
Pairs.

What you need
For the preparation: card, sticky tape, string, felt-tipped pens, scissors, plastic film.
For the game: two copies of photocopiable page 96, four large-necked containers of different sizes and shapes (as on the worksheet), two small yoghurt pots, two 'holds more' labels, eight sand-castle labels, damp sand, a sand tray.

Preparation
Draw a simple sand-castle on eight cards. Attach pieces of string, long enough to go over the children's heads and cover with film.

Cut two small labels from card to fit the boxes on the worksheet and write 'holds more' on them. Cover with film.

What to do
● Give each child a copy of photocopiable page 96 and one 'holds more' label.

● Show them the first two containers and ask them which one they think 'holds more'. When they have decided, they must place the 'holds more' label on the corresponding picture on the worksheet.
● Ask them to take one container each to the sand tray and use a yoghurt pot to fill it. Tell them to count each pot full of sand they use.
● When both containers are full, ask the players to compare the number of yoghurt pots used to decide which holds more. Ask them to look at their worksheet to see who has the 'holds more' label on the correct container. If anyone has guessed correctly, give him a sand-castle label to wear.
● Ask the children to do the same with the other two containers. The winner is the player wearing the most sand-castle labels.

Discussion
Why do the children think one container will hold more than another? Why it is important to use identical yoghurt pots to fill each one? Make sure that they understand that a full yoghurt pot must be exactly level at the top; this applies to the container as well. After the activity, let them compare all the containers to see which one holds most.

Load the trailers

Objective
To measure capacity using non-standard units.

Group size
Four.

What you need
Four toy vehicles with open trailers large enough to hold the non-standard units being used, four different types of non-standard unit such as marbles, beads, Lego bricks or Unifix cubes, pencils, small pieces of paper, a 1 to 6 die.

What to do
● Ask each child to choose a vehicle and one kind of non-standard unit.

● Give each child a pencil and paper and ask them to write down their estimate for how many units they think their trailer will hold.
● Let each child take turns to throw the die and put the corresponding number of non-standard units into their trailer.
● Continue the game until one child has filled his trailer.

Discussion
Towards the end of the game, ask the children how many more units they think they will need. Which non-standard units best fill the trailers? Which ones leave spaces and which ones do not? Unload the trailers and count how many non-standard units were used. Compare this with the original estimates. Who had the closest guess?

Calculators

Chapter eight

Many children come to school already familiar with calculators. Once they have an understanding of numbers to ten, calculators can be introduced in a structured way.

Encourage good habits from the beginning; teach children to use the fingers of their non-writing hand. Similarly, use specific calculator language such as display, clear and screen. Initially, children will need to use concrete apparatus with the calculator so that they make a connection between the two. As the appearance of numbers on the display screen is different to that most children are used to, it is wise to spend some time discussing the similarities and differences before embarking on any complex activity.

Calculator numbers

Objectives
To recognise the numbers on the display screen and to use the clear button.

Group size
Two to four.

What you need
For the preparation: white card, felt-tipped pens, scissors, plastic film.
For the game: calculators, used matchsticks, number cards 0 to 10, 'sad face' cards.

Preparation
Make a set of number cards, 0 to 10. Make two or three 'sad face' cards the same size as the number cards. Cover all the cards with plastic film.

What to do
• Give each child a calculator and make sure they know how to switch it on and off. Place the matchsticks within easy reach of all players. Shuffle the sad face cards into the number cards and place them face down in a pile.
• Ask each player to take turns to pick up a number card and press the corresponding number key on their calculator. Invite them to use the matchsticks to copy the digital form of the number on the display screen. Let them put the number card beside their matchstick number and press the clear button once they have finished.
• If they pick up a 'sad face' card, or if they pick up a card with a number they have already made, they must miss a turn.
• Let them continue until one player has made five numbers.

Discussion
Talk about when and where they have seen calculators used. Have they seen the digital form of numbers anywhere else? Count how many matchsticks each number uses. Are there any which use the same amount? Why is it important to press the clear button after each number? Encourage them to make a deliberate mistake and see what happens.

Crane game

Objective
To make a connection between the numbers displayed on a calculator and real objects.

Group size
Two to four.

What you need
A calculator for each child, an open lorry or trailer for each child, ten paper clips for each child, one large magnet on a string, Unifix cubes.

What to do
● Give each child a calculator and a lorry. Ask them to put ten paper clips into the back of the lorry, evenly spread out rather than all heaped together. Make sure the children know how to switch the calculator on and off and use the number and clear buttons.
● The first player must hold the magnet by the string like a crane and dip only once into the paper clips. Discourage them from dragging the magnet from

side to side. They should remove the paper clips from the magnet and count how many they have picked up.
● Ask all the players to put the total into their calculator. Once they have checked each other's screens, let them press the clear button.
● Let all the other players have a go. Then let them compare paper clips (by matching, if necessary) to see which crane has picked up the most. The player with the most paper clips must take one Unifix cube. A draw does not merit a cube.
● Let the children repeat the game until one player has collected three pieces of Unifix.

Discussion
If the children cannot count the paper clips in a random arrangement, encourage them to line them up and count from one end to the other. Does the magnet pick up more paper clips if they are heaped together or spread out? Let them experiment to find out. Which number is missing from the key-pad? How can that number be put into the calculator?

The farmyard game

Objective
To use a calculator for simple addition up to 20.

Group size
Two to four.

What you need
For the preparation: card, felt-tipped pens, scissors, plastic film.
For the game: calculators, small farm animals, a base board, a number die, small addition number cards, counters, Unifix cubes.

Preparation
Draw a large circuit on card and add linking pathways across the middle of the track. Divide the track into squares and alongside it draw animal enclosures, such as a pond, a barn and so on. Colour red the square adjacent to each enclosure and draw a small path leading to it. Colour the rest of the board and cover with film.

Make some small addition cards for the numbers 0 to 5 (see Figure 1).

What to do
• Give each child a calculator and make sure they understand how to switch it on and off, and use the + and = keys.
• Place the base board and the small cards (in a pile face down) within easy access of all players. Put a small number of farm animals (up to five) on each enclosure on the base board.
• Let each player take turns to throw the die and move their counter along the track according to the throw of the die. They can choose where to start and can move forwards or backwards.
• When they land on or pass over a red square, they must pick up a small number card and follow the instructions. For example, if the card shows +3, they must place three more similar animals onto the base board. The player must then say the addition number sentence before entering it into her calculator. For example, four sheep (press 4) and three more sheep (press + and then press 3 followed by =) is seven sheep altogether. Encourage the other players to use their calculators to check her as well as to count the animals on the base board.
• If she has entered the addition number sentence into the calculator correctly, she can take one piece of Unifix. If she is incorrect, the next player has a go.
• Let each player visit a different landmark and explain that she cannot return to the same one. Players can stop at enclosures already being visited by other players.
• Let them play until one player has collected five pieces of Unifix.

Discussion
Remind the pupils to press 'Clear' after they have entered a number sentence into their calculators. Praise children who 'count on' when adding up their animals. As more players visit each enclosure, do they notice what happens to the numbers they are dealing with? What is the largest/smallest total which any player calculates?

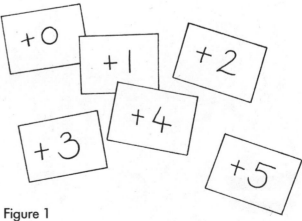

Figure 1

Clown colours, see page 14

Shape fish, see page 25

This page may be photocopied for use in the classroom and should not be declared in any return in respect of any photocopying licence.

Feeding time, see page 40

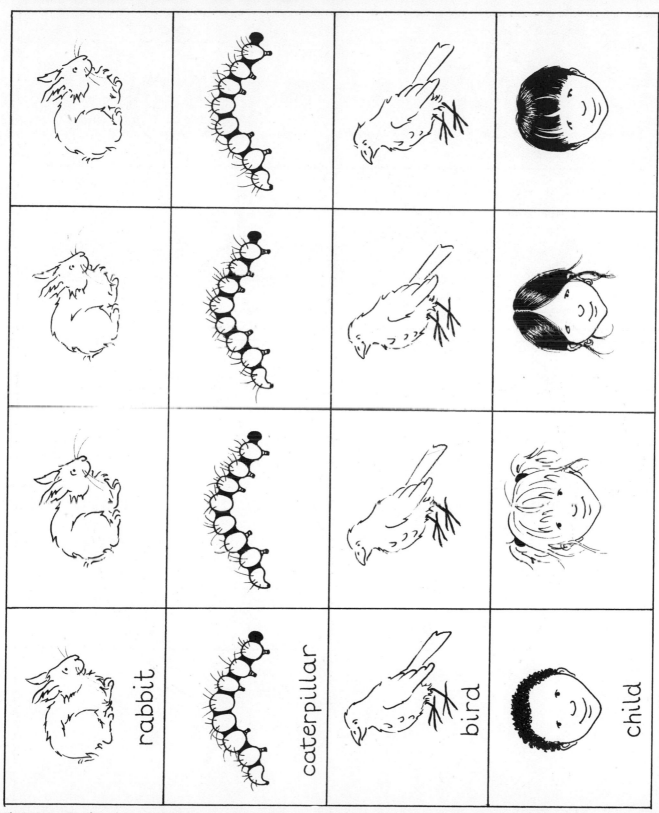

rabbit

caterpillar

bird

child

Spin the apples, see page 42

More	Less

Candles on the cake, see page 46

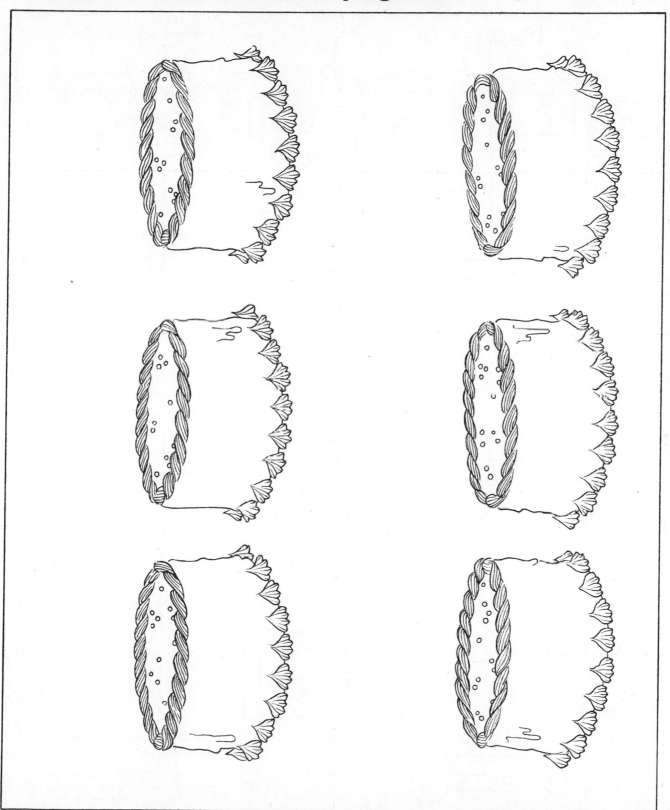

Robot buttons, see page 54

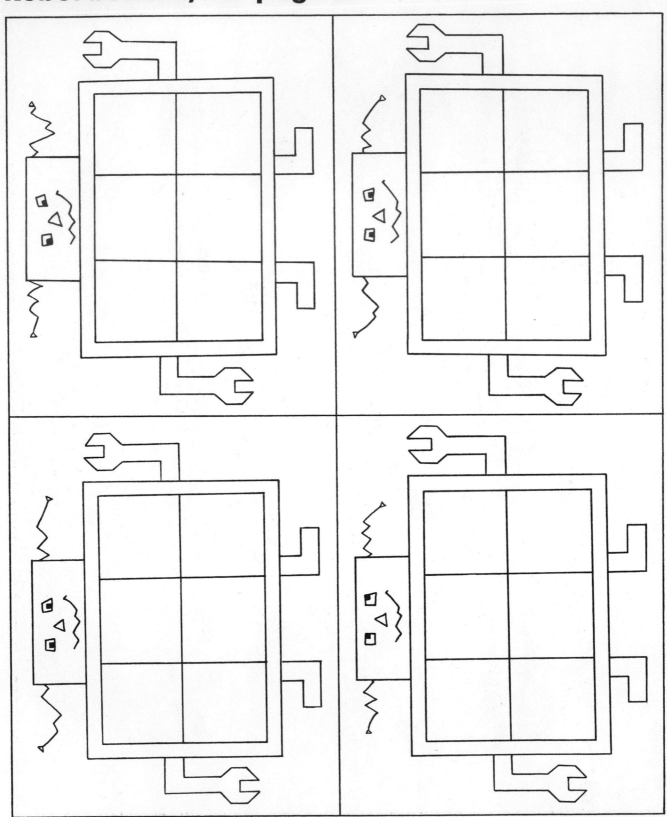

Money bug, see page 78

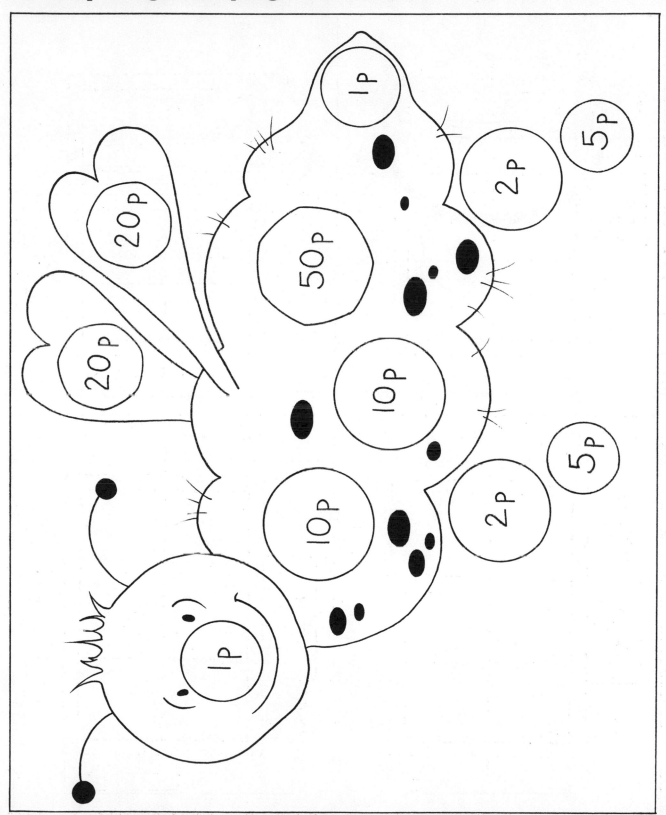

Sand-castles, see page 83

margarine

This page may be photocopied for use in the classroom and should not be declared in any return in respect of any photocopying licence.